LONDON'S LEA VALLEY
and the
GREAT WAR

Jim Lewis

LIBRI
PUBLISHING

The author Dr Jim Lewis taking a break during filming the story of the post-industrial revolution with the historian and broadcaster Sir Tony Robinson

Foreword by Terry Farrell

Jim Lewis is an extraordinary man. He is a traveller in that long tradition of indefatigable British explorers, journeying intellectually into unknown yet fascinating territory. Out of the glorious and chaotic metropolis which is London, Jim has discovered in his travels and revealed through his writing one of the great wonders of London – the extraordinary history of the Lea Valley.

The Lea Valley is the place where Jim spent his working life. The places he worked, and the characters he encountered there, drew him into the fascinating history of the place and inspired him to reveal the full story. I first encountered Jim through my own research into the Lea Valley, as part of my work in place-making and characterisation of the Thames Gateway. Little did I know I could spend a lifetime struggling to learn only a fraction of what Jim has discovered.

Jim is a relentless advocate for this extraordinary place. For many years, he has been campaigning to seek recognition for the significance of the Lea Valley as part of the rich history of London. For this small part of London changed the world – a crucible of scientific discovery and industrial firsts. His earlier books tell the unique story of the region, its scientists, engineers and entrepreneurs. But most significantly, Jim has revealed how the Lea Valley was the birthplace of the post-industrial revolution – the electronic technological revolution – which arguably began in the Lea Valley with the invention of the diode valve by Professor Ambrose Fleming. This small but inspired device allowed, for the first time, the control of a stream of electrons by electronic means, paving the way for modern electronic communication around the world and across the vast expanse of space.

Given the focus on the Lea Valley and the creation of the Olympic Park, Jim is unique in the way he has recognised the significance of the place. In this new book of the history of the Great War and the role of the Lea Valley's industries, Jim will make the connection between the scientists, engineers and entrepreneurs that worked in the region and I urge you to journey with him through a past which is shaping the future. It is people like Dr Jim Lewis who keep alive the magic of the place.

Sir Terry Farrell

Dear Reader

As the chairman of the RSA Trust, custodians of the former Royal Small Arms Factory, I am very honoured to be able to write the foreword to this book. I am also very grateful to Jim for all the work he has done to research and promote the remarkable history of the Lee Valley.

The importance of production and innovation in wartime is clear, but often the sacrifices made by industry, whilst acknowledged, are very rarely examined in detail in conventional histories of war. In this book Jim shines a light on the innovators, engineers and workers of the Lee Valley who maintained production on the home front.

The Royal Small Arms Factory was integral to the war effort, providing handsomely paid war work for many thousands of local men and women. The 24-hour shift patterns saw the four pubs surrounding the factory nationalised in 1915, to provide food and drink to all workers, some of whom commuted long distances to reach the factory, and in some instances worked 80+ hour weeks.

Many privately owned companies were also involved in the war effort. At the Lebus factory in Tottenham Hale production shifted from furniture to military material ranging from ammunition crates to the bodywork of the Handley Page Type O bomber. The old Lebus site is now Hale Village: a thriving community which provides homes and work for the people of Tottenham Hale.

I and my fellow trustees are proud to sponsor the publication of Jim's book. Since 2004 the RSA Trust has distributed over £3 million to good causes up and down the Lee Valley. It is funded from the surpluses generated by the regeneration of the Grade II listed old factory as a village centre of Enfield Island Village with shops, community facilities and business space. The site is managed along commercial lines by our sister company, RSA IV Ltd.

As the Royal Small Arms Factory trained young people through its world-beating apprenticeships, the RSA Trust now sponsors the Enfield Island Youth & Community Trust, developing young people around Enfield Lock from the ages of 0-19. The Factory (and others in the Lee Valley) employed women through the war; today the RSA Trust sponsors Enterprise Enfield's Inspiring Women programme, giving women the skills to succeed in business. Our excellent relationship with ex-apprentices of the Factory gives our small museum, the RSA Interpretation Centre an expert edge, with many unique objects and stories to tell within it.

This book of Jim's gives the region's wartime achievements the recognition they deserve.

Gary Walker
Chairman, RSA Trust
Enfield, April 2014

ABOUT THE AUTHOR

Dr. Jim Lewis has spent most of his career in the consumer electronics industry, apart from a three-year spell in the Royal Air Force servicing airborne and ground wireless communications equipment. When working in the Lea Valley for Thorn EMI Ferguson he represented the company abroad on several occasions and was involved in the exchange of manufacturing technology. Currently he is a Consultant to Terry Farrell & Partners on the historical development of London's Lea Valley and a Workers' Educational Association (WEA) tutor teaching industrial history. He also teaches students who have learning difficulties within the WEA's Community Programme. A freelance writer, researcher and broadcaster for his specialist subject – London's Lea Valley, he also has a genuine passion for encouraging partnership projects within the local community, designed to help stimulate social and economic regeneration. Dr. Lewis is married with four grown-up children and lives in Lincolnshire.

AUTHOR'S NOTE

In November 2013 I was approached by my publisher who enquired if I would be interested in writing a book to commemorate the centenary of the start of the Great War. He also emphasised that the book should highlight the role played by Lea Valley industries, its scientists and engineers in influencing the outcome of the conflict. Having already written eleven books and many articles about a region of Britain that I have an enduring passion for, how could I possibly refuse?

The Great War not only affected the industries of the Lea Valley region but also created a series of events that would affect the lives of everyone in Britain. Family lifestyles changed as new technologies entered the home and long-held practices in the workplace were destined to become redundant.

Over the years my research has shown that the Lea Valley is the birthplace of the post-industrial revolution, the technological revolution, with the invention and patenting of the diode valve by Professor Ambrose Fleming in 1904. It is the 'spin-off' from this technology, created in the region, that allowed the Allied Forces to detect the movement of enemy aircraft and shipping, the effect of which, arguably shortened the war and saved lives.

In writing this book I shall endeavour to set the scene for each chapter by including a brief history of the subjects under discussion. This will include some of my earlier research which has been updated to allow the Lea Valley Great War story to be brought together in one publication, not as a glorification of war, but as a celebration of the human spirit when faced with adversity.

Jim Lewis

DEDICATION

This book is dedicated to my family and also to my late mother and father, Leonora Maud Lewis and Walter Harry Portman Lewis.

ACKNOWLEDGEMENTS

The author wishes to thank the following organisations, companies and societies for their encouragement, support and advice and for supplying many of the illustrations within this book:

Alexandra Palace and Park Trust, Wood Green, London

BAE Systems, Farnborough, Hampshire

British Oxygen Company (BOC), Guildford, Surrey

Brooklands Museum, Brooklands Road, Weybridge, Surrey

Bruce Castle Museum, Tottenham, London

Cuffley Industrial Heritage Society, Cuffley, Potters Bar, Hertfordshire

Edmonton Hundred Historical Society, Enfield, Middlesex

Enfield Archaeological Society, Enfield, Middlesex

Enfield Business Centre, Hertford Road, Enfield, Middlesex

Enfield Local History Unit, Thomas Hardy House, London Road, Enfield, Middlesex

Epping Forest Museum, Sun Street, Waltham Abbey, Essex

Essex Record Office, Navigation Road, Chelmsford, Essex

Gunpowder Mills Study Group, Guildford, Surrey

Imperial War Museum, Duxford, Cambridgeshire

John Higgs, Freelance Historian, Fairford, Gloucestershire

Johnson Matthey, Brimsdown, Enfield

Lee Valley Regional Park Authority, Myddelton House, Enfield, Middlesex

London Borough of Enfield, Civic Centre, Enfield, Middlesex

London Borough of Haringey, Civic Centre, Haringey, London

London Borough of Newham, Town Hall Annex, Barking Road, East Ham, London

London Borough of Waltham Forest, Town Hall, Forest Road, Walthamstow, London

Mill Green Museum, Hatfield, Hertfordshire

Ministry of Defence Library, Royal Armouries, Leeds, Yorkshire

Museum of London, London Wall, London

Navtech Systems Ltd., Naseby Road, Market Harborough, Leicestershire

Newham Local History Library, The Grove, Stratford, Newham, London

Potters Bar Historical Society, Potters Bar, Hertfordshire

RCHME Cambridge, (National Monuments Record), Brooklands Avenue, Cambridge

River Lea Tidal Mill Trust, Bromley by Bow, London

Royal Commission on Historic Manuscripts, Quality Court, Chancery Lane, London

Southgate District Civic Trust, Southgate, London

Tesco Press Office, Delamare Road, Cheshunt, Hertfordshire

Thames Water, Gainsborough House, Manor Farm Road, Reading, Berkshire

The Greater London Record Office, Northampton Road, London

The Hackney Society, Eleanor Road, Hackney, London

The House of Lords Record Office, Westminster, London

The Institution of Engineering and Technology, Savoy Place, London

The Institution of Civil Engineers, George Street, London

The Institution of Mechanical Engineers, Birdcage Walk, London

The Marconi Archive, Oxford University Library Services, Oxford, Oxfordshire

The National Army Museum, Chelsea, London

The National Maritime Museum, Greenwich, London

The National Portrait Gallery, London

The National Archive, Kew, Richmond, Surrey

The Pump House Steam & Transport Museum, South Access Road, Walthamstow, London

The Royal Air Force Museum, Hendon, London

The Royal Society of Chemistry, Burlington House, London

The Science Museum, Kensington, London

The Waltham Abbey Royal Gunpowder Mills Company Ltd., Waltham Abbey, Essex

Tower Hamlets Local History Library, Bancroft Road, Tower Hamlets, London

Vauxhall Heritage, Luton, Bedfordshire

Vestry House Museum, Walthamstow, London

While many individuals have freely given their knowledge, some unknowingly, which has contributed greatly to the production of this book, I have, on a number of occasions paid special tribute to certain people in the footnotes of various chapters.

I could not let the occasion pass without recording my sincere thanks to my wife Jenny for her superb editorial skills and outstanding patience. The author freely admits that this voluntary sacrifice on Jenny's part has comprehensively tested the cement that holds our wonderful marriage together.

CONTENTS

INTRODUCTION

The question as to what caused the Great War (also called World War 1 and fought between 1914 and 1918) has been asked on many occasions. Reasons given in books and also by presenters of popular television programmes often suggest or promote the view that it was due to the assassination of Archduke Franz Ferdinand of Austria and his wife Sophie, Duchess of Hohenberg, while in Sarajevo on 28 June 1914. However, this analysis is too simplistic as most historians agree that the reasons were multifaceted and concerned nationalism, imperialism, militarism and common defence alliances. The assassination of the Archduke and his wife was the final 'spark' in a complex mixture of nationalism that ignited the conflict that set nations around the world against each other.

Decades before the Great War began several countries, particularly Germany and Britain, were engaged in an arms race. Germany had built up its High Seas fleet and Britain, which had always believed that Britannia ruled the waves, responded in kind. For centuries several European countries had gone about acquiring territories around the globe, particularly in Asia, Africa and the Middle East to extract their mineral and other wealth. This seems to have fostered an unhealthy belief amongst the colonisers that it was a normal way to behave and that the indigenous peoples of these countries were inferior and therefore deserved, or even needed, to be colonised. Once these interests had been established their wealth and trade routes required control and protection so overseas armies and governors were created. As Europe became more industrialised the need for minerals and other materials grew, setting off tensions amongst the colonisers.

As tensions mounted alliances began forming between the major European powers. In 1882 the Triple Alliance was formed between Germany, Austria-Hungary and Italy and in 1907 the Triple Entente was made between Britain, France and Russia. When the Archduke and his wife were assassinated all the tensions and territorial envy finally spilled over and the Great War began.

1. HOW AN UNLIKELY LEA VALLEY INDUSTRY AFFECTED AND WAS AFFECTED BY WAR

'Your country needs you'; Lord Kitchener encouraging able-bodied men to join the armed services.

An early chapter in *A Century of Growing*, my book about the history of the Lea Valley Growers' Association, represented wartime experiences that other industries and people probably encountered. It is therefore worthwhile reproducing most of the chapter here.

A story of the Home Front

On 4 August 1914, a little over two years after the formation of the Lea Valley Growers' Association, Britain declared war on Germany after the Germans had declared war on France and invaded Belgium. The effects of the conflict, which was to last until 11 November 1918, would throw up a number of substantial new challenges for the Lea Valley growers. Unfortunately the minutes of the Association are incomplete between February and September 1914 but we are given a clue about the shape of things to come from the October minutes when; 'A vote of thanks to Mr Dudding for his work as Secretary and best wishes for his success and safe return in military service' was proposed.

It was not just the national call to arms that was appealing to the patriotic spirit of the men of the Lea Valley horticultural industry; it was also another call coming from much closer to home that was causing concern amongst the growers. The minutes of the grower's meeting of January 1915 record that Mr Larsen had been appointed to 'see Colonel Fisher on the subject of curtailing the amount of local labour attracted to the powder factories to the detriment of the nursery industry'. One of these attractions was probably the better terms and conditions that manufacturing industries could offer the not so well paid workers employed in horticulture, a problem that would dog the Lea Valley growers for years to come.

Volunteers from all walks of life ready to sign up for military service (1914).

A tram in Fore Street Edmonton; trams were an essential part of the transport system during WW1, bringing workers to the factories.

Colonel F T Fisher R A was superintendent at the Royal Gunpowder Mills at Waltham Abbey, an explosives factory that had been in government control since 1787. During the Great War the mills were not only manufacturing gunpowder, they were also developing, producing and refining different types of explosives as well as certain chemicals. With pressure to increase the production of munitions coming from both government and the military, it is doubtful if the Association would have had any influence when confronting Colonel Fisher regarding the movement of workers from horticulture to the gunpowder mills. However, it is clear that the Association had thought of other ways that the problem might be tackled.

Colonel F T Fisher, Superintendent of the Royal Gunpowder Mills, Waltham Abbey (1909–1917).

At the October 1916 Annual General Meeting, the Secretary reported that through correspondence with various government departments they had been able to take 'an active part in getting skilled workers in the fruit growing section of the nursery industry classed as members of a reserved occupation'. This meant that should a worker receive his call-up papers for military service he could choose to remain with his employer. Now, through this recognition, certain members of the Lea Valley horticultural industry would be classed on a par with coal miners and other skilled workers whose jobs were seen as crucial to the war effort.

The labour problems concerning the growers would continue throughout the war as many of the industries in Britain had been taken over by government in an effort to increase production of munitions and other essential equipment for the allied forces and it was these manufacturers that were desperate for labour. This meant that horticultural workers who had not been granted reserved occupation status could either be conscripted into the armed forces if they were physically fit, or, if they failed their medical they might choose to work for one of these government-controlled industries which were probably perceived to have much stronger connections with the war effort than horticulture, not to mention the prospect of better pay.

A poster inviting women to join the Women's Land Army during WW1.

A poster to encourage daddy to join up for the Great War.

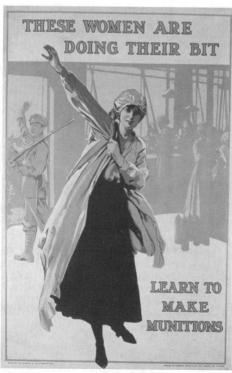

A WW1 poster encouraging women to take up a job in industry.

Women munitions workers manufacturing shell cases.

As thousands of men in the UK had volunteered or been conscripted to fight for their country, the jobs that they had vacated were taken over by women. The First World War is the first time in the history of Britain that women replaced skilled men in almost every workplace area (not just industry) and after a period of training were found to be equal to the work of men. While the minutes of the Association during the war years are not always regular, detailed or explanatory, particularly with regard to labour shortages and the employment of women, there are one or two clues that can be extracted from these records where conclusions can be drawn. For example, an instruction is given to the Secretary at the Association's AGM of November 1914 that he should 'write to the Belgian Refugee Committee and ask if they would be in a position to supply any horticultural labour for the spring time to local nurserymen'. The Council minutes of May 1916 record that a grower reported that he has 'received four summonses in respect of non-stamping of National Insurance Cards for temporary women workers'. These brief references would indicate that there were serious labour shortages amongst the nurserymen and also that growers were wrestling with new forms of legislation that they had never before encountered due to the employment of women.

Zeppelin L31 illuminated by searchlights after releasing bombs on glasshouses in Cheshunt.

In 1915 another wartime problem to beset the growers was the commencement of the world's first Blitz. This resulted in the deliberate targeting of the civilian population as the enemy tried to weaken morale and resolve, not just of civilians but of their relatives and loved ones fighting on the Western Front and elsewhere overseas.

On the night of 2 October 1916, one of Germany's new super airships, Zeppelin L31, commanded by the ace pilot Heinrich Mathy, was on a mission to bomb London. After making landfall at Lowestoft, Suffolk at approximately 8pm, he skirted the towns of Hertford and Ware as he made his way down country towards the Capital. North of Waltham Abbey Mathy came under intense fire from two separate anti-aircraft gun batteries; one of these was probably the one at Monkhams, positioned on the hill overlooking the Crooked Mile. To lighten the airship in an effort to gain height, Mathy released his complete bomb load in the hope of putting the Zeppelin beyond the range of the barrage from the ground. His descending missiles fell on Cheshunt, damaging over 340 houses and destroying some six and a half acres of glass which comprised all 40 glasshouses belonging to the Walnut Tree Nurseries.

Interestingly, the Association's 1911 minute book records a Mr J C Cobley residing at Walnut Tree House, Cheshunt. The minute book also shows that Mr Cobley was elected Honorary Secretary at the inaugural meeting, making him a member of the Association's Council. While the minutes of the Association for the First World War period are incomplete the minutes of the fifth AGM held on 20 October 1916 show a Mr G H Cobley being re-elected as Honorary Auditor. Also the minutes of the Association for 15 December 1916 record a Mr R S Cobley being in attendance. As it is likely that both of the Cobleys were related to the Association's founder member, Mr J C Cobley, this might suggest that they were probably connected, or perhaps lived, at the Walnut Tree Nursery. Therefore, it is surprising that there is no mention in the minutes of the Zeppelin raid that had wiped out an entire collection of a member's glasshouses. Could it be that the recording of such incidents was thought to be unwise, or perhaps such details were banned by the authorities in case the information fell into the wrong hands?

At a General Meeting of the Association held in December 1916, the President, Mr H O Larsen explained that the meeting had been specifically called to discuss 'potato culture under glass'. This was in relation to a conference he had recently attended, presided over by the Chief Inspector of the Board of Agriculture. After much discussion by the members a resolution was passed, with three abstentions, agreeing to dedicate an area of glass amounting to about five percent of the growing area of those nurseries with suitable soil for the cultivation of potatoes. This action would seem to suggest that the wartime sinking of merchant shipping by the German High Seas Fleet was beginning to have a serious effect on Britain's supplies which was no doubt being felt by the civilian population with the absence of food in the shops.

Reading the minutes of the May meeting of the Association in 1917 further evidence of food shortages can be deduced when it was reported that a number of members had received notices from the government requiring them to 'plough up all land laid down to grass since 1872 and sow the same with corn for the harvest of 1918'. The advice given by the Association to those who had been contacted was to return the form stating 'the impracticability of growing a successful crop of corn, or offering his land to the government according to the individual circumstances'. The attempt by government to get the Lea Valley growers to convert their land to cereal production coincided almost directly with the increased German U-Boat attacks on merchant shipping bringing supplies to Britain which had begun in earnest by March 1917. Many of these attacks were against American and Canadian supply ships as they crossed the North Atlantic and this action would eventually draw the Americans into the war in Europe.

The food shortages caused by the increased torpedoing of merchant shipping encouraged the British government to impose a system of rationing to help create a fairer distribution of staple foods across the population. It was also an effort to try and alleviate malnutrition that had been on the increase amongst some of the country's poorest working-class families. Sugar was the first foodstuff to be rationed in January 1918 followed by other commodities such as meat, butter, margarine, cooking fat and cheese. The population was issued with ration cards which had detachable coupons allowing for a weekly quantity of 15 ounces of meat, 4 ounces of fats and 5 ounces of bacon. Ration card holders had to register with a butcher and a grocer. While the weekly quantities might appear harsh it was a fairer way of food distribution as their introduction, along with price controls, made hoarding almost impossible and also helped to reduce the number of people queuing outside the grocers and butchers who were now allocated controlled amounts of stock.

Food was not the only commodity rationed during the war. Coal, a necessary fuel for heating the glasshouses of the horticultural industry and for generating the electricity that powered the factories that produced munitions and other essential goods while providing the motive power for much of the shipping and the railways, had been strictly limited for domestic use by wartime regulation. Premises with three to five rooms were allowed a weekly supply of 2 cwt, those with six to seven rooms 4 cwt, while those with over twelve rooms could have 8 cwt. It became an offence under the wartime

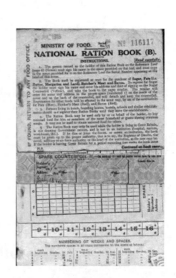

Rationing of food in Britain began in January 1918.

Domestic coal became rationed during WW1. This was to ensure that essential supplies were maintained for industry, shipping and the railways.

regulations to waste cinders and notices were published in newspapers of how to make briquettes out of coal-dust, clay and tar to use as a fuel for cooking purposes.

It would appear that the increasing shortages of food had pricked the conscience of the Lea Valley growers and this is reflected in the minutes of the January 1918 General Meeting, attended by 66 members. Guest speakers at the meeting were a Dr Keeble and Mr McKay who each spoke about the 'possibilities of nurserymen increasing the food supply of the nation at the present time'. Following the talk a resolution was passed that was carried unanimously to 'devote 5% of their glasshouse area to the cultivation of lettuces and radishes'. Some growers offered to 'grow cauliflowers as well'. While this initiative of the growers might not appear that significant to a 21st-century observer, it does show a collective responsibility on the part of the Association to support the nation at a time of crisis.

Parade outside Buckingham Palace to celebrate end of WW1 (1919).

The various requests from government to the Lea Valley growers to increase or diversify crop production to help supplement the nation's falling food stocks, allows us an insight into how quickly the Association had become established as a professional and respected body in the eyes of those running the country. Further confirmation of this can be gained from the Council minutes of April 1918 when a letter from the Board of Agriculture was read asking the Association to 'nominate a representative to serve on the proposed Horticultural Advisory Board'. Joseph Rochford was proposed in his absence and the motion was carried unanimously. (Mr Rochford was contacted from the meeting by telephone and agreed to accept the position.) These various approaches, made to the Association by government and other national bodies, give us a clear indication that the Lea Valley region had become an important and established part of Britain's food economy.

The period directly after the War saw the beginning of a slow return to normality for the Lea Valley Growers with the establishment of a Demobilisation Committee to ease the release of the male horticultural workers from their wartime industrial employment back to their peacetime occupations. This inevitably meant that women, who had been taken on to work in horticulture and other essential areas in place of men, would have to return once again to domestic life. However, the stage had been set; women had been recognised in the workplace as the equal of skilled men.

REFERENCES

Minute books of Lea Valley Growers' Association from 1911–1939

2. THE LEA VALLEY'S PART IN THE FIRST WAR IN THE AIR

The Great War (1914–1918) completely changed the way all future wars would be fought. The deliberate targeting of the civilian population in Britain opened up a new chapter of warfare with a strategy that was both inhumane and ruthless. This was not just about the death of innocent people and the destruction of property; it was also an attempt by the enemy to create fear, heighten anxiety and lower morale. It was a new tactic to increase the psychological pressure on vulnerable people at home in the hope of destroying the determination of a nation to overcome the threats of an aggressor.

The world's first Blitz

Many people believe that the world's first Blitz was the result of the German bombing of London and other major UK targets during the Second World War, the act of which engaged the Royal Air Force fighter squadrons in 'The Battle of Britain'. However, nothing could be further from the truth. In fact some of the most dramatic aerial encounters of the Great War occurred in Lea Valley air space and, according to the national press, the events were witnessed by many local people.

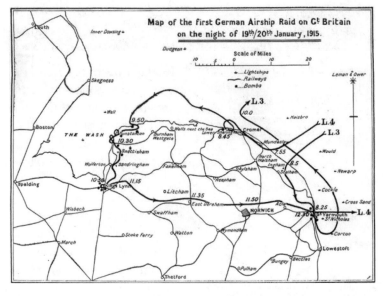

The first Blitz began on 19 January 1915 when two German Zeppelins dropped twenty-four 50 kg high explosive and a number of 3 kg incendiary bombs on the Norfolk towns of Great Yarmouth, King's Lynn and Sheringham, with some of the missiles falling on surrounding villages. As a result four people were killed and a further sixteen injured, with property damage estimated to be almost £7,500. This is the first time in history that civilians were deliberately killed by an enemy air strike. An additional nineteen air raids took place during 1915 killing 181 and injuring a further 455 people.

The first German airship raids on Britain were carried out in January 1915 by L3 and L4 on towns along the Norfolk coast.

The defence of Britain

The defence of Britain against aerial attack, for a combination of reasons, was slow to materialise. On 13 May 1912 the Royal Flying Corps (RFC), a branch of the Army, was formed and took over the responsibilities formerly held by the Air Battalion of the Royal Engineers, which included a balloon company.

A 1918 map showing London's defences with the Lea Valley region clearly visible.

In the first instance the responsibility for home defence had been divided between the Royal Navy and the Army and it was not until February 1916 that the latter was given full control. It would be easy to criticise the government and military authorities for not acting sooner but this was a new type of warfare and lessons had to be learned and strategies devised more or less on the hoof.

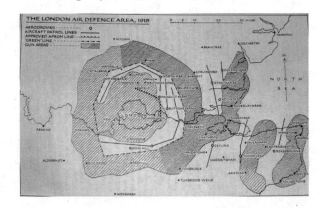

Initially there were no guns specifically designed for anti-aircraft purposes so existing weapons had to be modified and others, that could elevate their barrels sufficiently to

Damage to London the morning after a Zeppelin raid.

Anti-aircraft guns like this were not available to protect London at the start of WW1.

Leefe Robinson as a Lieutenant in the Worcester Regiment before he joined the Royal Flying Corps in 1915.

engage enemy aircraft, had to be ordered from France. Newly trained RFC pilots had to be taught fresh skills of how to fly and land aircraft at night and also ways had to be devised to allow airfield personnel to bring these rather elementary flying machines down safely. It should also be remembered that at the start of World War 1 the electronic technology for communication and navigation was at an embryonic stage of development and it would take another war to advance such technologies to a stage where they could reasonably be relied upon. In the beginning, only a few aircraft were fitted with the most basic wireless equipment that could only communicate one way, from air to ground, by the pilot tapping out Morse code messages while trying to fly his machine, often while fending off or engaging the enemy.

In the autumn of 1915, after the first air attacks on London in August by German airships, the RFC deployed aircraft to a number of airfields around the capital to bolster defences. These would help supplement the existing anti-aircraft guns and searchlight batteries. Now the different agencies would have to learn to work together and from this, new defence strategies would eventually emerge. Air raids on Britain continued throughout 1916 and it took the strengthened defence system a year before it achieved its first success.

Conflict over Cuffley: an attack from the air

On the night of 2/3 September 1916, Lieutenant William Leefe-Robinson, flying a BE2c biplane from Suttons Farm airfield in Essex, successfully brought down Schutte Lanz SL11, the first German airship to be destroyed in aerial combat over Britain. The airship crashed in a great ball of flame near the Plough public house in Cuffley, Hertfordshire with the loss of the entire crew of sixteen. Several eyewitness and newspaper reports of the incident referred to the airship as a Zeppelin and the mistake was further exacerbated by an over-enthusiastic press. One of the reasons why the Schutte Lanz burned so readily was because its internal framework was made of wood rather than the metal alloy duralumin, used in the construction of the Zeppelin.

Leefe Robinson in his BE2c aircraft after shooting down SL 11; two airmen are holding a wing section which Robinson had accidentally shot away in flight.

A Shutte Lanz 'E' type rigid airship that was the sister ship of SL 11 shot down over Cuffley.

The SL11 was one of a combined force of twelve Navy and four Army airships sent to attack London. It was commanded by Wilhelm Schramm, an experienced pilot who was born in England in 1855 when his father worked for the Siemens Company at Woolwich. Wilhelm was sent to Germany after the death of his father in 1900 and later joined the Army, progressing through the ranks eventually to the command of airships. In his first raid on London in September 1915, Schramm's was the only airship out of a group of four to release its bombs on the dockland areas of Greenwich, Deptford, Woolwich and Millwall. Perhaps his earlier knowledge of the region as a teenager helped him identify the targets. Accurately identifying landmarks from the air was one of the most difficult jobs that German aircrew encountered as they tried to locate their targets on dark, cloudy and foggy nights.

According to research carried out by Ray Rimell, an acknowledged expert on airship raids, Schramm crossed the River Crouch, Essex at 10:40pm on the night of 2 September and decided to approach London from the north. He flew over Chelmsford and Colchester then turned west towards Saffron Walden and continued his journey to London, flying over the Hertfordshire towns of Royston and Hitchin. Tracing the route of SL11 on a map this does appear to be an odd way to reach the Capital, but Schramm was an experienced pilot and may have reasoned that an approach from the east would have brought him into contact with the anti-aircraft defences much sooner than an attack from the north. As Schramm crossed London Colney, in an effort to gain height before reaching London's defences, he released six high-explosive and incendiary bombs that fell harmlessly in fields below. Continuing towards London, more missiles were dropped near Potters Bar, Enfield and Edmonton that killed three racehorses, damaged property and disrupted water supplies, but no human casualties were recorded. By 2:10am the airship was over Alexandra Palace, Wood Green and became illuminated by searchlight batteries allowing the anti-aircraft gunners to practice their recently learned skills. The rising flak caused Schramm to veer eastward across Tottenham. He then turned northward releasing twenty-four high explosive and three incendiary bombs on Ponders End and Enfield Highway that damaged several houses and ruptured a water main, but fortunately, again, there were no human casualties recorded.

SL11 was finally spotted by three pilots from No. 39 Home Defence Squadron who attempted to engage the airship but were unsuccessful. Lieutenant William Leefe-Robinson, who had just lost his prey, Zeppelin LZ 39, in cloud, gave up that particular chase and looked about for another opportunity. Seeing Schramm's airship illuminated by shell bursts he headed towards it. He came up underneath and emptied the magazine from his Lewis gun as he raked SL11 from stem to stern; the bullets appeared to have no effect. Breaking away, Robinson clipped another magazine of ammunition to his gun and proceeded to rake the envelope of the airship beneath once more; still no effect. In a final attempt Robinson decided upon a new strategy, this time concentrating all his fire in one place to the rear of the airship. This time he was successful as he observed a dull pink glow coming from inside the envelope. In Robinson's words, 'In a few seconds the whole rear part was blazing … I quickly got out of the way of the falling blazing Zeppelin and being very excited fired off a few red Very lights and dropped a parachute flare. Having very little oil and petrol left, I returned to Sutton's Farm landing at 2:45am. On landing I found that I had shot away the machine gun wire guard, the rear part of the centre section, and had pierced the rear main spar several times'.

Military personnel examine the remains of SL 11 before it is taken away for further inspection.

Crowds gather to pay their respects to the German aircrew of SL 11 who all perished on the night of 3 September 1916.

Crowds of Londoners and spectators across the Home Counties witnessed the demise of SL11. Although the time was after two in the morning people had been awakened by the drone of airship engines, the sound of bombs exploding, and the deafening noise from the gun batteries blazing away at the enemy. Upon going outside their homes they were not disappointed by what they were about to see. Reports suggest that when SL11 exploded in flames, the light was so bright it could be seen over a radius covering 60 miles, from Reigate in the south to Cambridge in the north. Newspapers, the following day, made much of the story and Robinson became a national hero literally overnight as his action had given flagging public confidence a much-needed boost. For the first time the public had witnessed that Britain had an answer to those leviathan invaders and their crews whom the popular press had dubbed 'baby killers'. For his gallantry Robinson was awarded the Victoria Cross. The announcement of the decoration came within two days of his success, one of the fastest recommendations in the history of the medal.

Below Left: The memorial to Captain Leefe Robinson VC at Cuffley, Hertfordshire; Robinson brought down the first German airship over Britain on 3 September 1916.

Below : Leefe Robinson's VC goes under the hammer at Christie's Auction House, London. The medal, in 1988, reached £99,000.

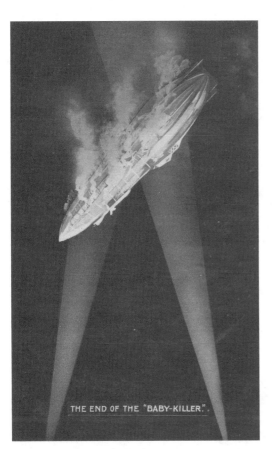

A propaganda postcard announcing 'The End of the 'Baby- Killer'.

Robinson's successful downing of SL11 was due to the new incendiary ammunition that had recently been introduced into the RFC squadrons. The bullets named after their inventors or manufacturers were known as Buckingham, Brock, Pomeroy and 'Sparklets', the latter after the popular soda siphon bulb. Normally the ammunition would be loaded into the gun's magazine as a mixture of rounds with normal 0.303-inch bullets. The idea being that the 0.303 round would pierce the airship's highly volatile hydrogen bags, allowing the gas to leak and mix with the air inside the envelope where it could be ignited by the incendiary bullets.

The Potters Bar Zeppelin

Almost a month after the downing of the Cuffley airship another victory was claimed in the skies over Hertfordshire with the bringing down of one of Germany's super Zeppelins, L31, at Potters Bar. This was a new breed of airship of massive proportion, with a length of just under 200 metres and a width of 24 metres. Although the top speed of these monsters was a little over 60 miles per hour they had an upper ceiling approaching 20,000 feet (6,096 metres), putting them easily beyond the range of the defending RFC squadrons and also the anti-aircraft batteries. However, these high climbers suffered severe disadvantages of extremely cold temperatures at altitudes that saw instruments and engines freeze. The rarefied air at these heights caused crew-members to suffer airsickness; fainting from lack of oxygen was often experienced and frostbite was not uncommon. To navigate and to identify targets, particularly if above cloud, the airship would have to descend, making it vulnerable to attack from both aircraft and guns.

A morale-boosting postcard that was issued at the time of the Zeppelin raids

On the night of 2/3 October Zeppelin L31 commanded by the German airship ace Heinrich Mathy was approaching London from the northeast. After making landfall near Lowestoft, Suffolk at around 8:00pm he proceed down country and at 9:45pm he was picked up by the Kelvedon Hatch searchlight.

Hark ! I hear a Zeppelin !

Zeppelin L31 that was brought down over Potters Bar on the night of 3 October 1916 by Lieutenant W J Tempest.

Mathy managed to avoid their attention by turning northwest before continuing his approach to London. He skirted around the towns of Hertford and Ware then, north of Waltham Abbey, he came under an intense barrage from two separate gun batteries. This forced Mathy to release his complete bomb load over Cheshunt in an effort to gain height away from his hostile reception. The bombs damaged over three hundred houses and destroyed six and a half acres of the Lea Valley horticultural industry's glasshouses.

Also on the night of 2/3 October Lieutenant Wulstan Tempest was airborne in a BE2c, patrolling a sector across the River Thames, backwards and forwards, from his home airfield at Sutton's Farm, Essex to another airfield at Joyce Green, near Dartford, Kent. Tempest's personal account shows that he was not too happy with his assignment as he remarked, '… the futility of being restricted to a ceiling of 8,000 feet, when it was common knowledge among those with experience of Zeppelin chasing that these ships rarely flew at an altitude of less than 12,000 feet, and often reached a height of 15,000 feet. How could one expect to 'pot' them with such a handicap?' Tempest decided to ignore his orders and changed course for central London, circling and climbing to gain height over the capital. Glancing at his watch he saw that the time was approaching midnight. Then, all of a sudden, searchlight beams began to penetrate the night sky and illuminate the unmistakable shape of a Zeppelin to the north.

Tempest estimated the airship to be fifteen miles away at a height of between 15,000 and 16,000 feet, on a heading towards London and diving at a steady rate as it flew. Turning his aircraft in the direction of the Zeppelin, Tempest flew towards her at about 90 miles per hour just as the anti-aircraft batteries opened up below. Ignoring the danger from the ground he pursued his quarry. At five miles from the airship Tempest was now higher than his prey and estimated the ship's height to be 'considerably below 10,000 feet'. As Tempest came closer he was caught in the middle of the anti-aircraft barrage with shells bursting all around him. Continuing his pursuit Tempest saw the Zeppelin release all her bombs; this would have been when the airship was over Cheshunt, as alluded to earlier. The airship's manoeuvre caused Tempest to believe it had been done specifically to gain height in an effort to shake him off, rather than to avoid the hostile gunfire from below.

Just as Tempest was about to engage the Zeppelin, the BE2c's petrol pump failed and he was forced to use the hand-operated pump, not the easiest of tasks while flying his machine and trying to engage the enemy! He was now flying very close to the Zeppelin and still slightly higher. Realising that his quarry could climb out of reach at any moment Tempest put his aircraft into a dive and came up underneath the airship strafing her with his Lewis gun as he flew beneath her. Although he was using Buckingham and Pomeroy incendiary ammunition laced with 0.303-inch ordinary bullets his strafing run had achieved nothing. Tempest made a second run beneath the airship from the rear this time putting in another burst from the Lewis gun; still no effect. Banking away from the airship and avoiding her hostile fire Tempest came round and placed his aircraft under the ship's tail

A picture of a gas cell inside a Zeppelin; incendiary ammunition had to be used by RFC pilots to ignite the hydrogen gas when it escaped.

section out of the way of her machine guns. While there Tempest let off another burst and this time he was successful as he saw a red glow coming from inside the Zeppelin's envelope, which he described as looking 'like an immense Chinese lantern'. How Tempest managed to fly and manoeuvre his fragile aircraft while hand-operating the petrol pump and aiming and firing his Lewis gun we shall never know; he was obviously a highly skilled pilot.

Removing bracing girders of L31 from tree; the military removed the remains which were taken away for examination.

As the fire took hold, the Zeppelin, in her death throes, shot upwards, probably due to expanding hydrogen in her gas bags and rose around two hundred feet, hung in the air for a few seconds and then began to fall. Tempest must have been mesmerised by the sight, as his description of the scene is one of awe. 'Flames burst from her glowing envelope and licked her bows. Brighter they grew, ruby orange, yellow, paler. And then she seemed to be coming straight for me'. Realising he was in mortal danger of being consumed by flaming debris and the falling leviathan he frantically put his aircraft into a nose dive to escape and was lucky not to be caught by the burning wreckage which he described as '… tearing down on me'. Tempest, thinking quickly, put his aircraft into a spin and managed to 'corkscrew' his machine out of the way as the blazing body of the Zeppelin roared past him. Still in awe of what he was witnessing, his eyes followed the flaming hulk all the way to the ground where on impact a cloud of sparks shot skyward. In his excitement Tempest fired off, 'dozens of green Very lights in the exuberance of [his] feelings'.

Coming round from the surreal experience, Tempest realised he had no idea where he was, he had no recollection of how long the Zeppelin engagement had lasted, neither was he sure how far he had travelled. As he wrote of the encounter, 'I had lost all sense of time and direction'. When analysing the experience some time later he wrote, 'I am firmly convinced now that I momentarily fainted in the air. When I came to, I imagined I was flying out to sea. I was positive I could see the grey waves below'. To try and identify where he was, Tempest brought his aircraft down to 5,000 feet and after a while he recognised the airfield at North Weald Bassett near Epping, Essex. Coming in to land, Tempest misjudged his height and overturned his aircraft, cracking his head on the butt of his Lewis gun. He was pulled from the damaged machine by ground crew and carried shoulder high in jubilation off the landing field. His injuries amounted to '… a slight cut and a bad headache which an X-ray examination afterwards showed to be a fractured skull '.

The tree that once stood in the driveway of No. 9 Tempest Avenue, Potters Bar, became known as the Zeppelin oak.

The next day Tempest made his way to Potters Bar to view the crash scene and although his experience seems somewhat ironic, by what he wrote of the occasion it would suggest that he was a very modest man. 'The blackened skeleton of the vanquished monster lay across two fields, and the enterprising farmer to whom they belonged was making a charge at the gate. I paid my shilling and went in'. For his gallantry, Tempest was awarded the DSO on 13 October 1916. Surely one would have expected, for his outstanding feat of heroism, that Lieutenant Wulstan Tempest would, like William Leefe-Robinson before him, have been awarded the Victoria Cross.

A new type of Blitz

By mid-1917 the Zeppelin invasion of Britain, which, for many reasons, is now regarded as generally ineffectual, was virtually over. Compared with the carnage on the Western Front, relatively few lives had been lost. However, the Zeppelin campaign had tied up scarce British resources, holding back over 17,000 men in defence of the Home Front who could have been deployed to reinforce the Allied troops in Europe and elsewhere.

After the scaling back of Zeppelin raids Gotha bombers began to attack Britain in 1917.

After the scaling back of Zeppelin raids the Blitz continued with the new heavier-than-air machines, the Gotha bombers. These aeroplanes posed a more terrifying threat than their predecessors. On 25 May 1917 twenty-one Gothas carried out their first daylight attack on Britain with a raid on Folkestone, Kent, killing 95 people and injuring 195 others. The following month, on 5 June, twenty-two bombers attacked Shoeburyness, Essex and Sheerness, Kent. On this occasion one of the raiders was brought down by anti-aircraft fire. 13 June saw the worst aerial attack of the War take place when London became the target. Fourteen (some estimates suggest eighteen) Gothas dropped up to 100 bombs, killing 162 and injuring 432 people. The attacks by aeroplanes rather than airships presented the RFC pilots with a new challenge. Unlike the Zeppelins, the Gothas, could not be seen from a distance and were only encountered when the RFC were on top of them. Now RFC pilots would have to develop and learn new skills. Sadly, this is the continuing story of war where each new technical development, when introduced, has to be 'trumped' by the opposing side.

REFERENCES

Bennett, J E, *The Story of the Potters Bar Zeppelin,* Occasional Papers No.1 (Potters Bar & District Historical Society, 2000)

Cole, Christopher & Cheesman, E F, *The Air Defence of Britain 1914 – 1918* (Putnam, London, 1984)

Liddle, Peter H, *The Airman's War 1914 – 1918* (Blandford Press, Poole, 1987)

Raleigh, W & Jones, H A, *Official History of the War: The War in the Air* Vols. 1-VI and Volume of Appendices (The Clarendon Press, Oxford, 1922–1937)

Rimell, Raymond Laurence, *Zeppelin! A Battle for Air Supremacy in World War 1* (Conway Maritime Press Ltd., London, 1984)

Taylor, John W R, *A History of Aerial Warfare* (Hamlyn Publishing, London, 1974)

Tempest, Major W J, *How I Shot Down the L31 Zeppelin,* The Journal of the Potters Bar & District Historical Society No.5 (Potters Bar & District Historical Society, 2000)

Note 1

During World War 1 only five airships were brought down over Britain: SL11, Cuffley, Hertfordshire, 3 September 1916, L32, Billericay, Essex, 24 September 1916, L33, Little Wigborough, Essex, 24 September 1916, L31, Potters Bar, Hertfordshire, 2 October 1916 and L48, Theberton, Suffolk, 17 June 1917.

Note 2

After the deaths of German airship personnel in Britain, they were usually buried in churchyards near to where the crash took place. In 1966 their remains were exhumed and laid to rest at the German War Graves Cemetery at Cannock Chase, Staffordshire.

Note 3

The first airship to be brought down in aerial combat during WWI was LZ37. The pilot responsible was Royal Navy Air Service (RNAS) Flight Sub-Lieutenant Reginald Alexander John Warneford. The Zeppelin was brought down over Ghent, Belgium on 7 June 1915 when Warneford released a number of bombs on her from above.

3. THE WORLD'S FIRST 'INVISIBLE' WAR – THE BREAKTHROUGH AT PONDERS END

Much has been written about the physical side of the Great War with graphic descriptions of flooded trenches, glutinous mud, unrelenting shelling, vicious barbed wire and the extreme suffering of both Allied and German troops. However, historians have paid less attention to the embryonic and emerging electronic technology that completely revolutionised the conduct of the Great War and would also dictate the pattern and strategies for all wars to come. This technology began life in the Lea Valley at Ponders End, Enfield and I claim that this is the birthplace of the post-industrial revolution, the technological revolution. While this was a world-changing event in media and communication terms, the technology was soon hijacked by the military authorities for creating new strategies in the killing fields of Europe and beyond.

Professor Sir Ambrose Fleming (1849–1945), the inventor of the diode (two electrode) valve, the world's first thermionic device.

Below right: *Guglielmo Marconi (1874–1937) an Italian electrical engineer who pioneered the development of wireless communication.*

Below : *Ediswan diode valve c. 1906 with a bayonet cap (BC) base.*

The electronic technology breakthrough

The big breakthrough in electronic technology came early in the 20th century, when, in 1904, Professor Ambrose Fleming, while working in the Lea Valley, invented the world's first thermionic device, the diode (two-electrode) valve. This was the first time that scientists had the control of a stream of electrons by electronic means (the multimedia industry of today can be traced back to this particular discovery). Fleming did not register his patent (No. 24850) until 1904; the device had been produced a few years earlier purely to understand the mechanisms that caused a blackening effect inside the glass envelopes of early incandescent electric lamps. Joseph Wilson Swan, the inventor of the incandescent lamp, had called in Fleming to examine the effect and his experiments were conducted at the Edison and Swan Electric Light works at Ponders End, Enfield. Fleming's subsequent work with the Marconi Wireless Telegraph Company, then based in Chelmsford, Essex no doubt caused him to think of improved ways of detecting wireless (radio) waves, which led him to retrieve his experimental devices from a cupboard at Ponders End. The breakthrough Fleming achieved can be seen as the beginning of the post-industrial revolution, the electronic technological revolution, as all today's familiar pieces of electronic technology can be traced back to that point in time.

Guglielmo Marconi arrives in Britain

In February 1896, only eighteen years before the world became embroiled in its first global conflict, Guglielmo Marconi, the inventor of wireless, came to England and, by August of that year, the War Office had arranged a conference to discuss the military implications of his inventions. Marconi gave a demonstration of his equipment by transmitting a signal over a distance of twenty yards between two adjoining rooms. Two days later Marconi carried out further experiments on Salisbury Plain. These were attended by the Post Office

Post Office engineers examine Marconi's early wireless equipment.

Chief Engineer, W H Peerce and Captain H B Jackson, later to become Sir Henry B Jackson, the First Sea Lord. Jackson, as an early wireless enthusiast, clearly had a good grasp of the future potential of this new medium, as he wrote of the occasion, 'It may be of interest to state that the energy consumed by this apparatus to transmit signals (two miles) at Salisbury was 13 watts, that for working the masthead flashing lamp being about 260 watts' (the masthead flashing lamp was an early signalling device used by the navy to communicate, by Morse code, from ship to ship and from ship to shore).

Over the coming months several demonstrations took place with experiments becoming more varied and more challenging. In 1899, before the military authorities at Aldershot, Marconi successfully demonstrated that wireless communication could take place between two tethered balloons spaced some distance apart, a landmark experiment before the arrival of powered flight. When powered flight finally arrived it would take scientists and engineers many years to perfect a successful system of inter-aircraft and aircraft to ground wireless communication. The magnitude of the problems to be overcome would prove to be truly astronomic.

Sir Henry B Jackson (1855–1929) attended Marconi's early wireless experiments on Salisbury Plain.

In 1899, during the Boer War, five sets of wireless equipment were sent to South Africa to provide ship-to-shore communication to assist the disembarkation of troops. The exercise, however, was beset with poor reception and other problems. For some unknown reason the War Office changed the original disembarkation plan and put the equipment directly into the field, then compounded their mistake by supplying the wrong aerial masts. Fortunately, the Admiralty must have been gifted with the power of foresight as they acquired three sets of the equipment. These were installed on Royal Navy ships and, during their 1899 manoeuvres, tests were carried out to check their suitability for wireless communication at sea.

A plaque on an old silk mill in Hall Street, Chelmsford where Marconi established his first wireless factory.

The Admiralty were obviously delighted with the results and orders were placed with the Marconi Company for a further twenty-six sets for Royal Navy ships and another six sets for their coastal stations. It would therefore seem fair to conclude that at least this branch of the military had recognised the value and the future potential of wireless. Not surprisingly there were some within the armed forces, mainly officer class from the old school, who remained sceptical of the usefulness of this new-fangled technology. Perhaps this scepticism can be likened to those modern-day people who refuse to use or trust the power and capabilities of computers!

While Marconi had shown the world (and the military) that it was possible to communicate by wireless across vast distances, it was not until Professor Ambrose Fleming invented the first thermionic device, the diode valve, at Ponders End, that the technology advanced to a completely different level. Before the diode valve, which gave scientists and engineers the ability to control a stream of electrons by an electronic means, the only way to detect an electromagnetic wave (wireless wave) was through a range of crude devices like the coherer. Fleming's breakthrough gave design engineers, for the first time, the technology to develop the thermionic valve further (by adding extra electrodes). The new electronic technology also gave engineers reliable and predictable results which would have been impossible to achieve with the earlier devices. It was this jump in the valve's development that led to the electronic multimedia world of commerce and entertainment we all enjoy today. Sadly, it has also projected electronic warfare forward at a rapid rate allowing battles to be fought from control centres thousands of miles away from the area of conflict.

Wireless experiments by the military

The years prior to the Great War saw many experiments by the military in wireless communication with equipment installations on land, at sea and in the air. Not surprisingly, as mentioned before, it was the latter that presented the greatest technical challenge. Apart from the weight of this embryonic equipment (up to 200 pounds), which could alter an aircraft's flying performance, not to mention the valuable space it could occupy in these very cramped early flying machines, there was the additional problem of the wireless spark transmitter presenting a potential fire hazard, as these early aircraft were constructed from highly flammable materials. Also, as might be imagined, there was the added requirement to generate sufficient power to run the equipment when airborne. Ways would have to be found to create a stable and reliable supply.

Stirling aircraft spark wireless transmitter WW1; these units could be too heavy for early flimsy aircraft and the spark was a fire hazard.

The introduction of the wireless caused major practical problems for the pilot too. Not only had he to fly and manoeuvre the aircraft when tapping out a message with a Morse key strapped to his knee but he also had to observe and report movements and other events on the ground. It was probably such difficulties that caused General Grierson to remark, during airship manoeuvres in August 1912 that 'the airship was of more use to me than the aeroplane, as being fitted with wireless telegraphy, I received messages in a continuous stream, and immediately after the observation was made'. Although the airship, as a weapon of war, had its own particular drawbacks, nevertheless it could outperform the early aircraft regarding the load it could carry and the electrical power it could generate for its wireless equipment. In August 1914, shortly after the British Expeditionary Force arrived in France, only three aircraft had been fitted with wireless equipment. At the time communication with these aircraft was only one way, from air to ground, and the medium employed was wireless telegraphy. This was Morse code and only spark transmitters were in use. The high levels of engine noise and vibration made it impossible for pilots to hear clearly the Morse signals sent by ground stations and this was why wireless communication was initially only practical one way. Successful speech communication was a few years away and this would require considerable experimentation by scientists and electronics engineers before satisfactory results could be achieved.

A Royal Aircraft Factory BE2c two-seater; these aircraft were often used for spotting for the guns.

Spotting for the guns

By the third week of September 1914, two aircraft fitted with wireless had been assigned to artillery observation duties and it is clear from early accounts that wireless technology was changing the way battles were planned and fought. The *Short History of No. 9 (Bombing) Squadron* tells us, 'The demand for the two wireless machines flown by Lewis and James became instant and Battery and Corps commanders were generous in their estimates of the value of their work'. Their work was 'flash spotting' (detecting the positions of enemy guns that were usually camouflaged) and also directing firepower (ranging). This helped to concentrate the shelling of the Allied Forces and more or less guaranteed target accuracy for the gunners.

British gun battery on the Western Front WW1.

Typically the operation worked by the artillery commander giving the pilot, before takeoff, the enemy targets he wished to destroy. A time between them would be agreed when the bombardment would commence. At the designated time the observing aircraft would appear over the Allied gun battery, the trailing wireless aerial (one hundred or so feet of copper wire with lead weights on the end) would be wound out, the transmitter switched on and a call made to the battery wireless operator indicating all was ready. Firing would commence and the pilot then observed the fall of shot. This was communicated to the gun battery wireless operator in a pre-determined code – 'Left', 'Right' 'Over' and 'Short'. Next there would be a pause while the battery commander re-sighted his guns and the fall of shot was again observed. Usually after a few such adjustments the pilot would signal 'OK', meaning a direct hit. The introduction of two-seater aircraft with an observer to carry out the task of spotting and communication was a godsend for the pilot, allowing him to concentrate on flying his machine and manoeuvring his way through hostile fire and avoiding the attention of enemy aircraft without the problems of operating the Morse key.

Observer adjusting camera before takeoff, WW1.

The limitations of early wireless

Wireless telephony (W/T), as mentioned earlier, the next major breakthrough in communication technology, had some way to go in its development before it would allow good two-way contact between aircraft and ground and also between aircraft. To do this required a continuous wave transmitter that allowed speech to be sent rather than Morse. The early spark transmitters, used for Morse, were technically incompatible with the new medium. The modulation of the continuous wave with speech would require the introduction of improved types of thermionic valve that allowed engineers the capability to design wireless receivers that were more sensitive and selective (the ability to gather weak signals and tune between stations on different frequencies).

Fleming's experimental diode valves were capable of the detection of early wireless signals.

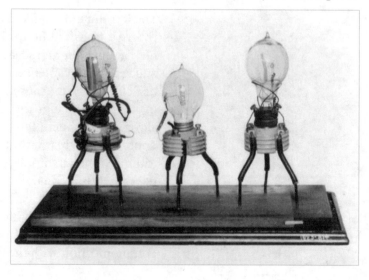

Lee de Forest (1873–1961) holding samples of triode valves.

While unquestionably a groundbreaking discovery, Fleming's diode was only capable of the detection of wireless signals (the ability to effectively allow an oscillating wave to flow in one direction) and could not amplify or become incorporated into circuitry that improved signal sensitivity and selection. These advances came later as engineers added further electrodes to the valve; the triode (three-electrode) was the next significant step forward. However, it took a war to further accelerate this technology as both sides strove to gain the military high ground. Interestingly the British public had to wait until 1922 to reap the civil benefits of the valve with the launch of the radio station 2LO by the British Broadcasting Company (the British Broadcasting Corporation (BBC) was not formed until 1926). Sadly it seems that war is behind the motivation for the advancement of many new technologies and one wonders how long society would have had to wait for the multimedia world of today without such sacrifices?

Design and development engineers recruited

The opportunity to take airborne wireless forward came when several Marconi engineers received wartime commissions and at least three of them, Major C E Prince, Captain Henry Joseph Round and Captain J M Furnival were heavily involved in solving the problems of aircraft speech communication. Round had considerable experience of valve development and it was probably no coincidence that he had been selected to work with his former colleagues. Most of this experimental work was carried out at Brooklands airfield, where No. 9 Squadron RFC had reformed in January 1915 under Captain H C T Dowding. The work of the engineers must have been relatively successful as Dowding recalled, when mentioning Prince: 'He evolved a wireless telephone in May 1915, and I believe that the first wireless telephone message was received by me at Brooklands during that month'. However, it was not until almost the end of the war, in July 1918, that two RFC squadrons on the Western Front were fitted with the latest wireless telephony (W/T) equipment.

Air Chief Marshall Sir Hugh Dowding who in 1915 was in command of 9 Squadron RFC. The squadron was involved in early wireless telephone trials at Brooklands.

The delay in equipping the RFC with the latest technology was because of major problems encountered in the design of suitable microphones that would allow clear speech to be sent above the roar and vibration of the aircraft engine.

An early carbon microphone.

Two German soldiers in 1917 displaying an interesting piece of listening headgear!

This meant designing appropriate microphone screening and making the devices capable of adjustment to cope with the differing levels of noise and vibration produced by different types of aircraft engine. It is probably fair to assume that Britain was ahead of Germany with this latest wireless technology. The evidence for this comes from a 'Special Order of the Day', issued by the German military, offering 10,000 Marks for a British aircraft compelled to land behind the German lines with its wireless telephone equipment intact. So concerned were the Allies that their new technology should not fall into enemy hands that aircraft fitted with wireless telephony were not allowed to fly over the German lines until the latter stages of the war.

American troops communicating by trench telephone system.

Early WW1 trench telephone.

German troops using field telephone; trench telephones often had their wires cut by heavy shelling.

Strategies change

Wireless completely transformed the way the Great War was fought by both the Allies and their German opponents. At the beginning the main method of communication on the ground was by telephone along an almost 500-mile front. Constant shelling continually cut the telephone cables and communication relied on runners, carrier pigeons and dispatch riders. The early introduction of portable crystal receiving sets (not requiring a battery) and portable battery-powered spark transmitters immensely improved communication between the troops in the frontline trenches and Corps headquarters situated some distance behind the lines. The Marconi Company was responsible for supplying much of this equipment to the Allies.

Knowledge sharing!

It might seem to the casual observer that Britain led Germany in wireless technology. After all, it was the British military and the Post Office that had supported Marconi's early experiments. However, research has shown that before and during the war years there was a considerable amount of in-depth technical material published in periodicals like the *Marconigraph*, *Wireless World*, *Aeronautical Engineering*, *The Aeroplane* and *Flight*. All this information was in the public domain so it would have been easy for Germany to keep abreast of some of the new technical advances.

The Marconi factory, New Street, Chelmsford (demolished 2013); as late as July 1914 Marconi and Telefunken engineers exchanged visits.

Telefunken Hannover building; prior to WW1 Marconi and Telefunken were in competition for government contracts.

Also, prior to January 1911, one of Europe's most formidable German wireless companies, Telefunken had been in direct competition with the Marconi Company for maritime contracts. On 14 January 1911, to overcome licensing and other contract difficulties, a joint holding company was formed out of Telefunken, Marconi and Compagnie de Telegraphie sans Fils of Brussels. The new company was called Deutsche Betriebsaesellschaft fur Drahtlose Telegraphie (D.E.B.E.G.) of which Marconi and the Belgian company had forty five percent interest and Telefunken the remainder. Here is clear evidence that both Britain and Germany shared knowledge of the evolving technology. It is also known that Marconi and Telefunken engineers exchanged visits as late as July 1914. Therefore, at the start of the Great War it must be assumed that the only probable technological advantage, for either side, would have been the amount of wireless equipment deployed on the battlefield. We know from the records that government placed only meagre orders with British manufacturers so wireless deliveries to the front were initially low. This would account for the use of the more traditional forms of communication at the beginning of the conflict. It also should be remembered, as alluded to earlier, that many of the commanders in the field were of 'the old school' and one would not have expected them to have been putting pressure on government departments for the new wireless equipment.

Code breaking – a new chapter of intelligence gathering enters warfare

Post card image of the high powered German wireless transmitter at Nauen.

When hostilities began in 1914, one of the first actions of the British was to cut the German links to the trans-Atlantic telephone cables, forcing Germany to rely on wireless as her only means of communicating with her far-flung colonies, with America and, most importantly, her shipping. It is probable that the Germans had anticipated the cutting of the trans-Atlantic cables as the power of the wireless transmitter at Nauen, just outside Berlin, had been considerably increased by the outbreak. This forced reliance on wireless by the Germans and created another chapter in technological warfare, that of signal encryption and code breaking, presenting a new range of intellectual challenges for both sides.

Further new countermeasures were developed when it became obvious that transmitting on the same frequency as your enemy (jamming) could seriously disrupt his ability to communicate and of course wireless opened up the possibility of deliberately feeding your opponent disinformation. The invisible war had really begun in earnest.

Admiral Sir Reginald Hall, Director of Naval Intelligence who had responsibility for code breaking and also for setting up Room 40.

It is clear that the British authorities had been unprepared for the hurried change in German communication strategy as it was not until late in 1914 that Captain (later Admiral Sir) William R. Hall, established what was to become the famous Room 40 in the Admiralty Old Building. It was there that Hall began assembling a growing number of cryptographers whose daily task was to decipher and analyse the intercepts arriving at the Admiralty from a number of different sources. It took time to bring together the right mix of people and to develop the skills needed to be able to play a meaningful role in the early days of signals intelligence gathering. However, from these modest beginnings, it was wireless technology that became the catalyst for the establishment,

through several metamorphoses, of today's famous Cheltenham establishment, Government Communications Headquarters (GCHQ), the British nerve-centre of signals intelligence (Sigint). It will no doubt be recalled that GCHQ has recently featured in a number of media reports over allegations of the establishment spying on the private electronic communications of innocent individuals allegedly unbeknown to the British government. This is a measure of how the technology of intelligence gathering has entered a new phase in the war of international vigilance against the threat of terrorism.

Old Admiralty Building from Horse Guards Parade. During WW1 the building housed Room 40.

No hiding place!

The Marconi Company had been particularly innovative during the early part of the war and had adapted some of its peacetime maritime wireless technology to aid the war effort. In November 1914 a small number of covered trucks left the Marconi Works in New Street, Chelmsford for France loaded with wireless direction-finding (D/F) equipment. The shipment was accompanied by experienced operators. Once set up the equipment was to prove invaluable to the Allies, as by the method of triangulation (using at least two D/F stations suitably spaced apart), any enemy wireless source could easily be pinpointed with a reasonable degree of accuracy the minute the hostile transmitter was switched on. This meant the enemy was now vulnerable to attack by guns ranged on their position or being targeted from the air by the Royal Flying Corps.

Below left: A wireless operator using a trench wireless receiver on the Western Front.

Below right: A mobile wireless transmitter and receiver developed for use on a wagon; the weight of the equipment with its batteries caused wagons to sink into the battlefield mud.

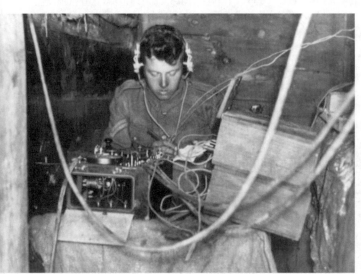

To track the movements of the German High Seas Fleet, the Marconi Company had constructed a line of direction finding (D/F) stations along the east coast from Kent to Scotland. The Marconi engineer H J Round was mainly responsible for the D/F stations' design and development. How successful these D/F stations were and the value of the emerging technology can be gauged by considering the strategy employed by the Admiralty during one of Britain's most famous sea battles, the battle of Jutland.

While the D/F stations were monitoring naval wireless traffic of the German High Seas Fleet, it was noted that her principal wireless ship the *Bayern* and those answering her had moved 1.5 degrees, a particularly precise measurement considering this technology was still in its infancy and the electronic components to improve sensitivity and accuracy had yet to be developed. Remarkably, this small movement suggested that the German fleet had moved from its base at Wilhelmshaven and had taken up a position in the Jade River and was about to put to sea. It is likely that the D/F station at Hunstanton, on the Norfolk cliff top, was one of those involved with triangulating the bearing. What is also remarkable is that the distance between Hunstanton and the German fleet was almost 300 miles.

Captain Henry Joseph Round, the Marconi engineer responsible for much of the design and development of direction-finding equipment.

The information of the movement was communicated, via landline, to the Admiralty's Room 40 and the Grand Fleet, under the command of Admiral Sir John Jellicoe, was ordered to sea a day early so that advantage might be gained over the German Battle Fleet by forcing an early engagement. The following day, 31 May 1916, the battle of Jutland commenced. This is just another example of how wireless changed the way war was fought.

The east coast D/F stations, almost by luck, could also detect the position of the deadly 'U' Boats when they surfaced to use their wireless and they could also follow the course of Zeppelins as they crossed the North Sea on their way to carry out bombing raids on designated targets in Britain. Zeppelins had the advantage of being able to fly high; the later super Zeppelins could get above 20,000 feet, which could keep them out of range of attacking aircraft and the gun batteries below. However, on many occasions the height advantage turned into a serious disadvantage for the German aircrews, as

A naval operator who appears to be using a temporary direction-finding station that would track enemy shipping and aircraft.

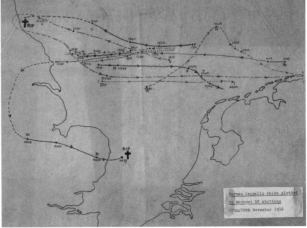

Map showing the plotting of Zeppelin movements by Marconi direction-finding stations.

instruments and equipment would freeze, rendering its operation useless. And on cloudy nights it was impossible for the crews to navigate a course by sighting familiar landmarks. When this happened the airship would have to resort to calling base for a wireless bearing to discover their location.

A Zeppelin wishing to find its position would usually call the German control centre at Cuxhaven (in Morse code) giving its particular call sign, normally a single letter, and request permission to obtain a bearing. Once granted, the Zeppelin would transmit the letter 'V' which the wireless operator would repeat for about thirty seconds. The Zeppelin's signal would be picked up by at least three fixed German D/F stations and the respective bearing between each of these and the airship would be taken. In turn these D/F stations would communicate their results to the control centre by wireless where, by triangulation, the position of the Zeppelin would be plotted on a large-scale map. It was normal for the German D/F stations to communicate their bearings to the control centre by wireless and the centre would then pass the details to the Zeppelin. Once the information was received it would allow the navigator to plot his own position. However, it was usual for the control centre to enquire if the Zeppelin had received the information and if not the message would be repeated on higher power.

The enemy wireless traffic was a gift gratefully received by the Marconi east coast D/F stations allowing the Zeppelin's course to be monitored as it crossed the North Sea. This information was communicated to Room 40 in London where the progress of the invader and any others on the raid was regularly plotted on a chart. As the different bearings were received the plots were moved across the chart and this not only allowed Room 40 to calculate the Zeppelin's position but also its airspeed. It was known that once over Britain the Zeppelins would have to descend to bombing height and this would render them vulnerable to attack by British aircraft as well as artillery.

Map of Western Front 1918 showing how wireless communication had expanded by the end of the War.

Room 40 collated the information passed from the Marconi D/F stations and it was then a simple task to alert the appropriate fighter stations and gun emplacements that were close to the incoming Zeppelin's path. Aircraft would be scrambled and were ready and waiting as the enemy approached. Observers on the ground would be on heightened alert listening for the first characteristic drone of a Zeppelin's engines, while the searchlight batteries and gunners anxiously waited for their opportunity to engage.

Without the use of wireless, the strategies described above could not have been employed and it leaves one wondering what would have been the outcome of the Great War had this new technology not come along when it did. It is doubtful if Ambrose Fleming could have foreseen, even remotely, the invisible war that his invention would bring about when he created the world's first thermionic device at a lamp works in Duck Lees Lane, Ponders End, Enfield, in London's Lea Valley.

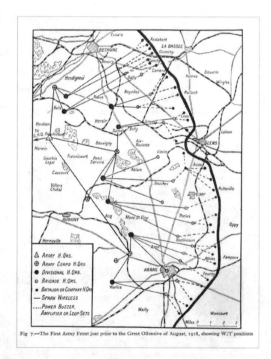

Fig 7.—The First Army Front just prior to the Great Offensive of August, 1918, showing W/T positions

Appendix

The prolific Edwardian author, the late Harold Begbie, wrote a manuscript that he had intended to be published as a book entitled, *Wireless*, or possibly *Wireless in the War 1914-1918*. Sadly it was never published, because of warnings to his publisher from the military intelligence services.

Unfortunately the timing of the proposed book coincided with a state of national nervousness as the intelligence services did not wish to let other countries, particularly Russia, know how much information we held on encryption.

Harold Begbie had wished to dedicate his book to the young wireless operators, many of whom he had interviewed after the war, as he saw them as unsung boy heroes. In the second paragraph of his introduction he succinctly captures the essence of the new wireless technology when he writes:

> *Their book, which I have the honour to write, may also be called a history of the war that was never seen, that was both invisible and inaudible even to those who fought its battles, a war that was as immaterial as thought, as unsubstantial as dreams, as ethereal as personality.*

REFERENCES

Admiral of the Fleet Sir H B Jackson, *Direction and Position Finding: discussion* (The Journal of the IEE, Vol. 58, Part 3, 1920)

Author unknown, *The Marconi Book of Wireless* (Marconiphone Company, London, 1936)

Author unknown, *Aircraft* (copy of article dated 4 June 1919, in the Marconi Archive, Bodleian Library, Oxford)

Baker W J, *The History of the Marconi Company* (Methuen, London, 1972)

Beesley Patrick, *Room 40, British Intelligence 1914-1918* (Hamish Hamilton, London 1982)

Furnival, J M, *The Development of Wireless Technology in the RAF, 1918* (Marconi Archive, Bodleian Library, Oxford, n.d.)

Lewis, Cecil, *Sagittarius Rising* (Davies, London 1936)

Lewis, Jim, *London's Lea Valley, Britain's Best Kept Secret* (Phillimore & Co. Ltd., Chichester 1999)

Lewis, Jim, *The 'Weeding' of Harold Begbie* (Intelligence and National Security, Volume 9, No. 1, Frank Cass, London, January 1994)

Lieut. Colonel A G T Cusins, R E, *The Development of Army Wireless During the War* (The Journal of the IEE, Vol. 59, 1921)

National Archive, Kew, Air1 688/21/20/9 *(1915-1937) Short History of No. 9 (Bombing) Squadron*

Round H J, *Direction and Position Finding (with discussion)* (The Journal of the IEE, Vol. 58, Part 3, 1920)

4. WIRELESS COMMUNICATION AND SPY HYSTERIA ON THE HOME FRONT

At this stage in the book we shall take the opportunity to journey around Britain to examine a little-researched area of the Great War and this will show how Professor Ambrose Fleming's inspired device added, quite unintentionally, to the atmosphere of panic and suspicion that was already building in the minds of the general public.

From the beginning of the 20th century until the start of the Great War, fiction writers supported by the 'Northcliffe Press' had engendered a belief within the British people that the country contained a network of German spies. Professor Christopher Andrew in his book, *Secret Service*, illustrates quite vividly the general mood of the population created by these literary story tellers when he says, 'Though the real war in Germany was to be delayed until August 1914, it was preceded by over a decade of fictional conflict'.

The literary war began in earnest in 1903 with Erskine Childers best-selling novel, *The Riddle of the Sands*. While yachting off the

Early amateur wireless equipment.

Friesian Coast, the heroes of the novel, Carruthers of the Foreign Office and his companion Davies, gradually uncover a German invasion plan. Andrew goes on to say that the writer William le Queux and the ageing military hero Field Marshal Earl Roberts of Kandahar ran successful campaigns against both imaginary invaders and spies. To bring home to the reader the atmosphere that Andrews is trying to describe, I shall take the opportunity to quote a short passage from one of le Queux's books, *The Invasion of 1910*.

> *In a moment the superintendent had taken the operator's seat, adjusted the ear-piece and was in conversation with Ipswich. A second later he was speaking with the man who had actually witnessed the cutting of the trunk line.*
>
> *While he was thus engaged an operator at the farther end of the switchboard suddenly gave vent to a cry of surprise and disbelief.*
>
> *'What do you say, Beccles? Repeat it', he asked excitedly. Then a moment later he shouted aloud:*
>
> *'Beccles says that German soldiers – hundreds of them – are pouring into the place! The Germans have landed at Lowestoft, they think'.*
>
> *All who heard these ominous words sprang up dumbfounded, staring at each other.*
>
> *The assistant superintendent dashed to the operator's side and seized his apparatus.*
>
> *'Halloa-halloa, Beccles! Halloa-Halloa-Halloa'*
>
> *The response was some gruff words in German, and sounds of scuffling could distinctly be heard. Then all was silent… But what held everyone breathless in the trunk telephone*

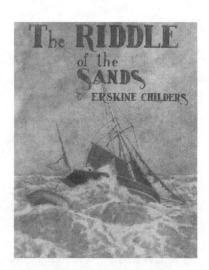

Erskine Childers' Riddle of the Sands, the book that induced spy hysteria.

headquarters was that the Germans had actually affected the surprise landing that had been predicted by the military critics; that England on that quiet September Sunday morning had been attacked. England was actually invaded. It was incredible.

Therefore, by the time war broke out the stage was set, the thoughts firmly planted in people's minds, to interpret hitherto innocent actions of friends and neighbours as communicating information to the enemy. Research at the National Archives, Kew has uncovered a host of incidents which although highly amusing in the light of today, do reflect a sad side of British society, which seems to have suffered a form of spy hysteria or brain-washing.

Replica of the Marconi radio room on RMS Titanic.

Newspaper headline with the word Wireless that featured in the arrest of Crippen.

The influence of spy stories, coupled with the common knowledge which was openly available to all through newspapers and periodicals of the evolving technologies of war like the airship, aeroplane and submarine, not forgetting the well-armed German Fleet, heightened people's awareness and fears. In 1914 by the start of the Great War wireless was an accepted fact. In previous years the medium had made newspaper headlines on a number of occasions with various rescues at sea. The most notable of these was the rescue of survivors after ships were alerted by distress signals put out when the Titanic struck an iceberg and sank in 1912 with considerable loss of life. Another well-publicised story was the dramatic arrest of the murderer, Dr Crippen and his mistress, Ethel le Neve, in 1910, following a wireless message from *S.S Montrose* to New Scotland Yard. Couple these events with the relative ease by which nations of the world could communicate with each other by wireless and it does not take too much imagination to understand what people's minds could have been experiencing at the time. Their imaginations were dreaming up ideas about foreign-looking men in dark coats with turned-up collars communicating with aircraft and warships to rain destruction on their homes.

An American poster warning the public to watch what they say.

To get some idea of the magnitude of the hysteria, it is worth examining the official 'Reports of Alleged Enemy Signalling in Great Britain (1914)', held at the National Archives, Kew. The records indicate that reports of enemy signalling began to come at the commencement of the War and rapidly increased in number. There were other reports of concrete enemy gun platforms disguised as tennis courts or factory machine beds. Petrol stores for hostile submarines were a further source of alleged enemy activity. The three classes of report remained throughout 1914–1915, but by the end of the period, concrete beds and petrol stores had vanished, but signalling still persisted.

Many reports of enemy signalling were not recorded, although Scottish Command provided over two thousand and Southern Defence Army, several hundred. Around eighty-nine percent of all cases investigated were cleared up, leaving eleven percent unsolved. It would appear that in twenty-two percent of the cases investigated, suspicion was aroused solely by the nationality of the alleged signallers.

It might be helpful to refer to two instances of spy hysteria, from Hugh Cleland Hoy's book, *40 O.B How the War was Won*, in order to help the imagination sense the atmosphere that existed at the time. Incidentally, Hoy was in a privileged position to observe these matters as he was private secretary to the Director of Naval Intelligence, between November 1916 and December 1917 and it was said that he was entrusted with Admiral Jellicoe's most confidential correspondence.

Because of their intensity at night, lights feature quite regularly in spy stories. The following incidents as reported by Hoy might seem amusing when considered today, but at the time they were deadly serious. His first report concerns the manager of one of the principal hotels in Scarborough, who happened to be of German origin. He was suspected of signalling from the hotel's top floor by light to hostile aircraft or other raiders. The matter was investigated by an officer from Scotland Yard, who discovered that the on-off signalling by light was caused by people opening and closing a top floor lavatory door.

The second report concerns a house in Crowbridge, Sussex, where the occupants, two old ladies, were said to be sending Morse signals to the enemy. One night these elderly occupants answered a knock at the door, only to find their property surrounded by an armed detachment. The signalling problem had been caused by a tree branch flapping in the wind. Hoy substantiates evidence in the National Archives when he says, 'all reports were followed up no matter how stupid'. The overall view taken by the investigating authorities was that signalling to the enemy did not take place and if it did, communicating with aircraft would be almost impossible, given the difficulties experienced by the early flyers.

As an example of both hysteria and signalling difficulties, one report at the National Archives quotes an incident of a naturalised alien who incurred suspicion of signalling to the enemy after crashing his motor car into a fence within the grounds of his house, some two days before a Zeppelin raid. The day after damaging his car he had erected an arc-light to prevent a similar accident and was therefore accused of signalling. Hysteria must have been particularly overpowering as the report states, that 'at five to six thousand feet, Zeppelins are unable to distinguish lights of different magnitude'.

Pigeons as a means of communicating with the enemy had been discounted by the military. As the report states, 'British pigeons would not fly to a German loft' and the military had also said that, 'no pigeons had been allowed into the country'. I think that the last quote must refer to pigeons coming into the country in crates or baskets, rather than those making their way here on the wing! Lights, rockets and heliographs (by day) are also mentioned in this report and again mainly discounted. However, page seven of the report is somewhat puzzling when the view is expressed that wireless as a method of signalling is unlikely.

RMS Titanic showing the two wireless masts; by 1912 most ships crossing the Atlantic carried wireless equipment.

WW1 poster campaign warning of female spies!

Although the authorities investigating the reports of enemy signalling by wireless thought its use to be unlikely, I have not discovered any evidence to suggest that they had really thought through all the ramifications concerning this means of communication. If we accept that one of the commoner and possibly the easiest form of communications investigated was by flashing lights, then it would not be unreasonable to assume that the recipients of these signals, being either, airships, aeroplanes, submarines or ships, would in turn have to relay these messages to their own intelligence services. Unless, that is, the crews of these vehicles waited until they returned to base; an unreasonable assumption in my view as the speed of communication was of the essence. In this particular scenario wireless would have been the only method that the enemy could have used to relay its messages back for analysis and action. Even if the British intelligence authorities thought wireless communication by enemy agents unlikely, the public making the allegations of spying could not have believed so. Although there was no national broadcasting service in Britain during the period of the Great War (BBC Radio was not established until 1922) the public were well aware of wireless as a communications medium as it had been around since the beginning of the century and headline-grabbing examples have already been given in this chapter.

Early Marconi Morse spark key.

As further evidence of wireless communication that was in the public domain I shall take the opportunity to quote from correspondence which appeared in early 1915 in the popular magazine, *Wireless World*. Here, a Mr J B Tucker, the secretary of Birmingham Wireless Association, a body comprising of amateur wireless enthusiasts, responded to reports that appeared in the press regarding the Court Martial of Archibald George Cocks, on 6 December 1914. Cocks had been charged with having wireless apparatus in his possession without permission. Tucker writes:

> *I should be glad if you would publish this letter in your next issue, as I am anxious that it should serve the purpose of dispelling any bad impression which might be caused among*

this gentleman's friends through seeing the average news paper reports, as well as acting as a warning to any amateurs who may still have wireless apparatus in their possession. The President of the court stated:

(A) That no charge of communication or attempted communication with the enemy was being brought forward. The G.P.O [General Post Office] witness read a letter to the court from the Postmaster General stating that, as the accused was a British subject, he had no desire to press the case. The same witness stated that the portable set in question was only capable when connected to the necessary aerial and its present condition of transmitting for one mile. The necessary aerial and station in general were, of course dismantled in the ordinary way by the G.P.O people at an earlier date, when all wireless stations were similarly treated. The station, therefore, was 'reasonably incapable of being worked'.

(B) 'Mr Cock's character was not doubted, and that no evidence to the same need be brought'.

Nevertheless, our Mr Cocks was sentenced to six months imprisonment, four months of which were remitted owing to him having served seven weeks in custody. Because it was felt that Cox had only committed a small technical offence it was stated by Tucker, 'the unwarrantable severity of this sentence is obvious'. Later in his letter Tucker says, 'A short time ago a German was sentenced to three months detention without hard labour for having a wireless station on the Essex coast. The German referred to was an un-registered alien, and his apparatus was connected to the mains and was capable of sending over one hundred miles'.

As I have already explained I have only quoted from the Tucker letter to illustrate how simple it would be for the public of the day to imagine the ease with which spies and agents could communicate by wireless, particularly as a network of amateur enthusiasts was already in existence. It will no doubt have been noted that Tucker's letter implies that bias and sensationalism exists in the popular press. In fact the press was considered to be a fruitful source of information for any spy or agent. Articles appearing in the daily newspapers could give clues to how the Allied Forces were faring in the War, thereby giving any astute spy the opportunity to communicate information back to his own intelligences services. Of course there was always the possibility for the British intelligence services to feed the press with misinformation.

Brigadier General Macdonogh, who was Director of Special Intelligence and General Headquarters (Intelligence), was chiefly concerned with the 'publication of undesirable material, such as soldier's letters to the press'. One particular letter, which appeared in *The Times* on 21 January 1915, suggested 'relative exhaustion of French manpower'. *The Times* was prosecuted for publishing the letter, but in the ensuing court case on 5 June 1915, the authorities lost, owing to, 'certain legal technicalities'. The report, to be found at the National Archives within the history of M17 (a body specialising in censorship), indicates the real fear of the authorities who saw the press as communicating sensitive information to the enemy. The case was also seen as a loss of face for the government. One can see how deeply the loss of this particular court case was felt from the following quotation, 'To the destructive criticism which at this period this group of newspapers brought to bear on war policy of the Government and the conduct of operations in the field, the Foreign Office attributes much of our loss of prestige in neutral countries'. What also comes out of this incident is a clear indication of the Northcliffe Press's attitude to censorship, even in time of war.

It would seem simple to imagine how the intelligence services of the day viewed certain information appearing in the press which was derogatory towards the Allies, knowing this could be communicated speedily to the enemy by wireless. After all, the Germans, it would appear, seemed to have anticipated future wartime communication problems when they constructed a high power wireless transmitter at Nauen just outside Berlin as early as 1906. This really came into its own when the British cut the German trans-Atlantic cable links in August 1914, forcing the enemy to use the airwaves.

Germany had also established a chain of wireless stations within forty-one states of the American Union, four more in Mexico and another sixteen spread throughout South America. This set-up becomes more impressive when it is borne in mind that the powerful German wireless station situated on Long Island opposite New York, had increased its power at the start of the Great War by almost three hundred percent. Therefore, taking these few examples of Germany's ability to communicate over very long distances by wireless, it is easy to understand how sensitive the British intelligence services were to stories, or even hints, appearing in the press regarding the progress of the War. This makes it is easy to understand the desire of the intelligence services for censorship.

REFERENCES

Andrew, Christopher, *Secret Service* (Guild Publishing, London, 1985 pp. 36-38)

Author unknown, *Marconi Jubilee 1897-1947* (The Marconi Wireless Telegraph Company Limited, Chelmsford, Essex, 1947 p.13)

Author unknown, 'Wireless Telegraphy in the War', *Wireless World*, Vol. 2, April 1914 – March 1915

Bright, Charles, *Telegraphy Aeronautics and War* (Constable & Company, London, 1918 pp. 42-44)

Cleland Hoy, Hugh, *40 O.B How the War Was Won* (Hutchinson & Co., London, 1932 pp. 95-97)

Le Queux, William, *The Invasion of 1910* (Eveleigh Nash, London, 1910 pp. 9-10)

National Archives, Kew, *Reports re Alleged Enemy Signalling in Great Britain, 1914*. Reference Air 562/16/15/66

National Archives, Kew, *Military Press Control, History of the Work of M17 (1914-1919)*, Reference W032 9304

5. THE INCREDIBLE MRS HILDA HEWLETT

Over the years the Lea Valley has had its fair share of outstanding women working within the region from Annie Besant of Match Girls fame to Nancy Tate, MBE, who founded the OEDA charity to campaign about and also to research the causes of asbestosis (mesothelioma), a lung disease normally contracted through long-term low-level exposure to the material asbestos. Hilda Hewlett deserves to be placed up there with her other Lea Valley colleagues, particularly in this centenary year of the Great War.

Hilda Beatrice Hewlett was one of nine children born in Vauxhall, South London on 17 February 1864 to Louisa and the Reverend William Herbert. When she was a young woman Hilda attended the National Art Training School in Kensington where she studied needlework, woodwork and metalwork. It is likely that these latter two subjects set her on a path towards what she would become in later life.

Hilda Hewlett not dressed for flying posing with aircraft at Brooklands.

At the age of twenty-one Hilda trained as a nurse at a hospital in Germany and three years later, in January 1888, she married Maurice Henry Hewlett in her father's church, St Peter's Vauxhall. The couple produced two children, a daughter Pia and a son Francis.

In October 1909 Hilda attended the first official aviation meeting to be held in the UK at Blackpool and it was probably here that she became besotted with the relatively new craze of flying. Interestingly, A V Roe, the Lea Valley flyer, was also present at the Blackpool event but on this occasion he had failed to get his aircraft airborne!

Hilda's new-found enthusiasm for aviation can be seen from her next move, as soon after the visit to Blackpool she made her way to the Mourmelon-le-Grand airfield in France where she began the study of aeronautics. While there, she made the acquaintance of Gustav Blondeau an aviation engineer and in 1910 they opened Britain's first flying school at Brooklands, Surrey. Here they trained many people to fly, one famous name being Thomas Sopwith who became a prominent aviator and aircraft builder in his own right. On 29 August 1911, Hilda became the first woman in Britain to gain a pilot's certificate (No. 122). Hilda even went on to train her son Francis to fly, and in November 1911 he gained his pilot's certificate (No. 156).

A warmly dressed Hilda Hewlett in front of an early flying machine.

Hilda Hewlett flying certificate photograph.

Hilda Hewlett standing by a rather flimsy aircraft.

The Hewlett and Blondeau workforce beside an Avro 504 at the Legrave factory, Luton.

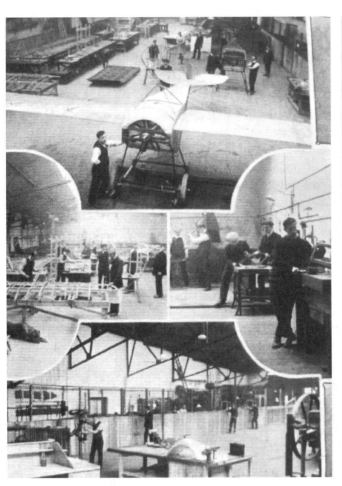

Hewlett and Blondeau's first aircraft factory, formerly an ice-skating rink, Clapham, London.

Hewlett & Blondeau's factory Legrave, from Flight *magazine, 1915.*

Hewlett and Blondeau established an aircraft manufacturing business, managed by Hilda, first at Brooklands, named Hewlett & Blondeau Limited, building aircraft under licence. Later the business moved to larger premises, at an old skating rink at Clapham Junction, South West, London, and was known as the Omnia Works. In May 1914 the business moved again to a ten acre site at Leagrave, Bedfordshire in the Lea Valley. During the Great War the factory employed 700 workers that built over 800 military aircraft, all under licence. What is remarkable is that the records show that there were ten different types of aircraft being built, no mean feat for a new start-up factory. One of the aircraft built was the now famous Avro 504, which became the backbone of the Royal Flying Corps during the Great War. So the connection with Avro was made once again.

Towards the end of the war the Air Ministry were becoming concerned about the manufacture of one of their aircraft that employed a particularly powerful 90-horsepower engine and they decided to appoint a Mr Ashley Pope to oversee the Leagrave operation. On arrival Pope discovered that Hilda, who was running the factory, was working an almost twenty-four-hour day without even stopping for meals. If this were the case it would seem that the Air Ministry were right to have concerns as a tired manager could have, through lack of attention, caused a possible loss of quality and production efficiency. Hilda and Maurice had separated in 1914 after Hilda had caught the flying bug; this and her passion for aircraft manufacture would appear to be the reason for the breakdown of the marriage. However, the breakdown could have been more to do with what would now be considered the outdated attitude of Maurice, who was alleged to have said 'Women will never be as successful in aviation as men. They have not the right kind of nerve'. From what we have learned, Maurice had clearly underestimated the drive, determination and considerable flying skills attained by his wife!

After the war, with orders from the Ministry of Aviation for military aircraft at an end, the Hewlett & Blondeau, Omnia Works returned to one of their pre-war areas of expertise, that of agricultural engineering. They also began the manufacture of a range of industrial engines to power machinery. By 1920, with Hilda now in her late fifties, the decision was taken to close the Works and the machinery was put up for sale, some being sold to local companies, one of these being Vauxhall, the motor vehicle manufacturers in Luton. The Hewlett & Blondeau factory site at Leagrave was eventually sold to Electrolux, the manufacturer of popular household electrical appliances.

It would seem that Hilda had decided, after the factory was sold, that a complete change of lifestyle was required away from the long hours and the pressures of working at senior and management level within industry. In 1931 Hilda emigrated to Tauranga, New Zealand, soon afterwards her children and their families followed. Perhaps Hilda's yearning for a quieter life was just a dream after all, as the spirit of aviation had clearly not left her. In 1932 Hilda became the first president of the newly formed Tauranga Aero and Gliding Club. However, it is believed that apart from her new aeronautical connections, she enjoyed an outdoor life of camping and fishing, her family affectionately giving her the nickname 'Old Bird'.

Hilda died in New Zealand in 1943 at the age of 79. For her outstanding contribution to aviation, and particularly to her aircraft manufacturing work during the Great War, the name Hewlett has been recognised in road names both in New Zealand and Luton.

REFERENCES

Hewlett, Gail, *Old Bird the Irrepressible Mrs Hewlett* (Matador, Leicester, 2010)
Flight Magazine, 11 June 1915

6. THREE MILLS COMES TO THE RESCUE OF THE ALLIED FORCES!

Arthur James Balfour (1848–1930), Foreign Secretary in David Lloyd-George's wartime government.

Strange as it may seem, Three Mills, situated at the southern end of the Lea Valley in the London Borough of Newham, at Bromley by Bow, was very much involved in helping the Allied war effort. The site history of Three Mills can be traced back to at least the 11th century, when it was recorded in the Domesday Book that there were nine mills in existence. Later some of the mills would have been owned by the Cistercian order of monks from the nearby Abbey of Stratford Langthorne, as their grounds covered the area.

In the early part of the 20th century a young biochemist left his native Russia for England, first taking up a university teaching and research post in Manchester. Apart from his academic career, he was passionately committed to Zionism, working tirelessly to establish a homeland in Palestine for the Jewish people.

By 1914, the pressures of political activity and academic work were beginning to weigh heavily upon him. Returning from Switzerland in August that year, he found a War Office circular on his desk. The document invited scientists who had made discoveries of possible military importance to submit them to the UK Government. Unknown to him at the time, the event was to mark a significant turning point in his career.

The biochemist had previously worked on a fermentation process, the significance of this will be revealed later, and he made details of his experiments available to the Government, generously asking for no remuneration. Nothing was heard until the spring of 1916, when the biochemist received a visit from Dr Rintoul, the chief research chemist of Nobel, a leading explosives manufacturer. Rintoul checked the biochemist's laboratory notebooks, which contained his experimental work. After this, arrangements were made for the director of Nobel's to come to Manchester with two of his chemists. The fermentation experiments were successfully repeated and a contract was offered and accepted. Alas, soon afterwards, the Nobel Scottish plant suffered a serious explosion and the company was released from its contractual obligations.

In March 1916, the biochemist's university career was interrupted once more when he was approached by Sir Frederick Nathan, the head of the Admiralty powder department. Nathan asked for help and explained that there was a serious shortage of acetone, a solvent used in the making of Cordite, a smokeless explosive made from gun cotton. The challenge was immediately taken up by the biochemist, who spent four days of his week in Manchester and the remaining three in London to set up a pilot plant to manufacture the solvent and this is when the biochemist's fermentation process was put to good use. The project was of such national importance that the biochemist was released from his university duties to concentrate on assisting the war effort.

Later the biochemist was introduced to Winston Churchill, then the First Lord of the Admiralty, who explained: '…we need thirty thousand tons of acetone', and asked: 'Can you make it?'

With powerful people like Churchill behind him, the biochemist was able to assemble a team and find new premises for his large-scale pioneering experiments. The plant chosen was the Nicholson gin distillery, housed in the Clock Mill at Bromley by Bow, the site currently known as Three Mills.

Winston Spencer Churchill (1874–1965); during WW1, when First Lord of the Admiralty, Churchill asked Chaim Weizmann if he could manufacture 30,000 tons of acetone.

After many months of disappointment the process was finally capable of regularly producing half a ton of material. When the Admiralty was satisfied with the results, arrangements were made to convert several distilleries in Britain to the new process. A programme was then rapidly put in place to train chemists to run these new production plants. Later, owing to wartime shortages of grain, a main ingredient in the acetone distillation process, a large part of the production was transferred to Canada and other countries where plentiful supplies of the cereal existed.

While these activities were going on, the biochemist, Dr Chaim Weizmann, had become recognised as a prominent figure in the British Zionist cause, becoming leader of the World Zionist movement by 1920. Working for the Admiralty during the Great War had brought Weizmann into contact with many powerful people including Arthur James Balfour who had replaced Sir Edward Grey as the UK Foreign Secretary. In November 1917, Balfour issued his famous Declaration giving Britain's support for the establishment of a Jewish national home in Palestine. So apart from Weizmann's pioneering work at Three Mills in developing a process to support the manufacture of explosives that were vital to the war effort he was also an influential figure in establishing a homeland State for the Jews. Lloyd George in his memoirs has written the following passage which is quite revealing:

The Clock Mill at Three Mills, Bromley-by-Bow; this is where Dr Chaim Weizmann tested his process to manufacture acetone in bulk.

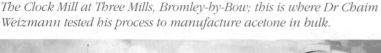

Dr Chaim Weizmann (1847–1952) who became the first President of Israel.

When our difficulties were solved through Dr. Weizmann's genius, I said to him: 'You have rendered great service to the State, and I should like to ask the Prime Minister to recommend you to His Majesty for some honour'. He said: 'There is nothing that I want for myself'. 'But is there nothing we can do as a recognition of your valuable assistance to the country?' I asked. He replied: 'Yes, I would like to do something for my people'. He then explained his aspirations as to the repatriation of the Jews to the sacred land they had made famous. That was the font and origin of the famous declaration about the National Home for Jews in Palestine.

As it has been said about many world-changing events, and we shall repeat it here about this particular one, 'the rest is history'.

In 1948 Weizmann was rewarded for his hard work and dedication, when he was elected the first President of the State of Israel. So it could be said that a little-known site at the foot of the Lea Valley (Three Mills at Bromley by Bow) has played an influential part in world history, first by helping the Allies secure the peace during the Great War and secondly by promoting the career of this now famous man.

REFERENCES

Gardner, E M, *The Three Mills – Bromley by Bow* (The River Lea Tidal Mill Trust, London 1957)

Lewis, Jim, *London's Lea Valley, Britain's Best Kept Secret* (Phillimore & Company Limited, Chichester 1999)

Lloyd George, David, *War Memoirs*, Vol. 2 (Odhams Press Limited, Watford 1933)

Weizmann, Chaim, *Trial and Error the Autobiography of Chaim Weizmann* (Hamish Hamilton, London 1949)

7. DEVELOPING THE NEW EXPLOSIVES AND THE ROLE OF THE ROYAL GUNPOWDER MILLS, WALTHAM ABBEY

By the middle of the 19th century there was a growing need for an explosive more powerful than gunpowder, as the size of guns increased, through advances in manufacturing machinery and technology. These improvements in artillery weapons, not unreasonably, caused the demise of Congreve's gunpowder rocket for battlefield purposes as the missiles could be unreliable particularly in gusty wind conditions. However, Congreve rockets were adapted for other important uses such as firing safety lines to ships in distress during rescues at sea and for signalling purposes. Some were adapted as parachute flares and the development of this latter device saw its importance grow at the time of the Great War.

A poster by the YWCA appealing for funds to set up hostels and canteens for women war workers.

Women workers with hand-propelled wagons used for moving material around the Royal Gunpowder Mills site.

Women munitions workers in protective clothing at Royal Gunpowder Mills.

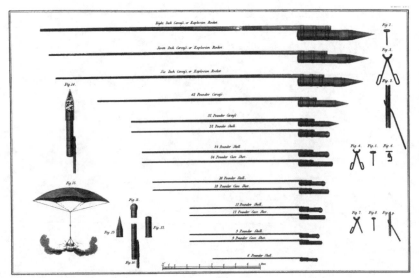

Diagram of Congreve rockets, note the image on the left of an early parachute flare.

A Very pistol for firing signal and illuminating cartridges.

Sir Frederick Abel (1827–1902) was responsible for improvements in the manufacture of gun cotton, particularly at Waltham Abbey.

During the Great War Very lights, a development of Congreve's parachute flare, were used to illuminate battlefields to good effect. The Very light was developed by an American Naval officer, Edward Wilson Very (1847–1910) and were fired skyward from breech-loading snub-nosed pistols or from trench mounted tubes. The flare's purpose was to illuminate the battlefield at night to allow the gunners to fire upon enemy positions or on advancing troops. This is a prime example of how later generations of engineers and scientists continued to perfect and develop earlier technologies. The next example in the development of explosives can be seen as evolving in a similar way to Congreve's invention.

On the Continent, gun cotton, a mixture of nitrating acids on raw cotton, was emerging as the new powerful explosive. Production however was slow and hazardous. In 1863, Sir Frederick Abel, the War Office Chief Chemist set up an experimental plant at Waltham Abbey to test his ideas regarding the safe production of gun cotton. His experiments were successful and the end product proved stable, which gave him the ability to manufacture large quantities of the material. Perhaps the greatest compliment to Abel was that his process was widely copied and the product was welcomed not only by the military but also by civil engineers who put it to use for blasting in quarries and mines and also in the construction of roads and tunnels.

Sir James Dewar (1842–1923), the joint inventor with Sir Frederick Abel of the essential WW1 explosive, Cordite.

In 1847 the Italian chemist Ascinao Sobrero, working under T J Pelouze at the University of Torino discovered Nitro-glycerine, a highly volatile liquid explosive formed by the combination of glycerol and nitric and sulphuric acids. In 1867 the Swedish chemist, Alfred Nobel was able to combine Nitro-glycerine with absorbent clay and his invention became Dynamite. In 1890 Sir Frederick Abel's Explosives Committee, which included the talented chemist Sir James Dewar, devised a new propellant by adding nitrating acids to glycerine and combining the mixture with guncotton and mineral jelly to form what became known as Cordite. Abel and Dewar patented the invention on behalf of the British government. Apart from devising an explosive that was more stable than some of the earlier materials, it could now be manufactured in long cords by extrusion from a hydraulic press, hence the name Cordite.

A Ruston Proctor narrow-gauge locomotive pulling Cordite wagons at the Royal Gunpowder Mills.

Women operators working alongside men at a Cordite press at the Royal Gunpowder Mills c. 1916.

In the early 20th century, under the Directorship of Colonel Sir Frederic Nathan, Waltham Abbey saw many improvements in the production of Cordite and gun cotton. Nathan also introduced improvements that were designed to increase efficiency and save money. One of these was a new recovery process for acetone, a solvent used in the manufacture of Cordite. It will be recalled that at the southern end of the Lea Valley Chaim Weizmann was developing his process at Three Mills, Bromley by Bow to produce large quantities of acetone from grain.

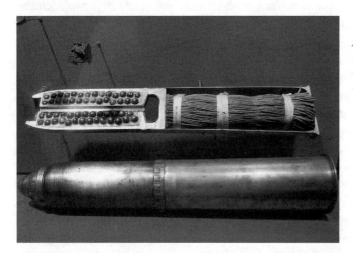

WW1 eighteen-pounder shell showing cut-away with simulated bound strands of Cordite.

Under Nathan the nitration plant was redesigned for the production of Nitroglycerine and he also introduced new plant for the booster explosive, Tetryl. The improvements and expansion at Waltham Abbey, the only government explosives factory at the time, were, to say the least, opportune, as they allowed large quantities of explosives to be manufactured for the Allies during the Great War.

Apart from the sad human losses and carnage created by war, there is always an inevitable outcome; that of the rapid increase of technological change brought about as one side strives to gain a major advantage over the other. The Great War saw, for the first time, the coming together of two relatively new technologies, that of the aeroplane and wireless. The Second World War was to prove no exception to this rule. As each of the belligerents fought for technical supremacy pushing forward the developments in radar, jet engines and explosives at an accelerated rate, an unusual twist to the story took place. The rocket as a weapon of war came back onto the agenda, not quite in the Congreve format as used against military targets, but in the shape of the V1 and V2 rocket programme, this time in a more powerful form to be used against a civilian population. Ironically the development was now by German scientists who were leading the world in this secret research.

REFERENCES

Lewis, Jim, *From Gunpowder to Guns the Story of Two Lea Valley Armouries*, (Middlesex University Press, London 2009)

8. THE ARCHAEOLOGY OF THE FIRST BLITZ

In 2006, as industrial historian for the Great War Archaeology Group (GWAG), I was able to persuade my colleagues to carry out an archaeological survey and dig of sites in London's Lea Valley region that had, at the time of the Great War, played a vital role in the defence of Britain. As we have already learned from previous chapters, a considerable amount of aerial warfare took place in the sky above the Lea Valley and also that the authorities had taken steps to build a protective ring of gun emplacements, searchlight batteries and airfields around the north east side of London. While much of the dig focused on the Lea Valley region, other sites, a Zeppelin crash site in Suffolk and another at North Weald in Essex, were included to complete the overall archaeological picture and also to get a better understanding of how the first Blitz took place.

Dr Neil Faulkner opening up structure 'B' on the Monkhams Hall gun emplacement site during GWAG dig.

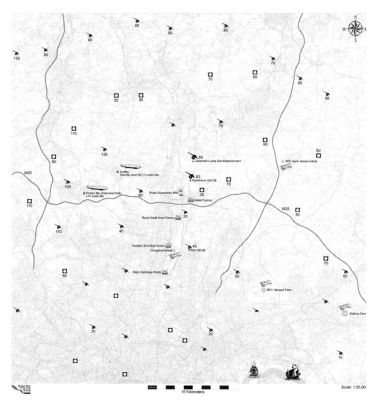

As the desktop and preliminary field research plus the task of carrying out this dig was estimated to take several weeks, Dr Neil Faulkner, a director of the GWAG, managed to secure part-funding for the field-work from the commissioning editor of the BBC2 *Timewatch* television programme. *Timewatch* filmed the archaeologists working and unearthing finds at two of the dig sites, one in the Lea Valley and one in Suffolk.

Viewers of popular television archaeology programmes mainly see the work of the diggers, metal-detectorists and the geophysics teams; they seldom get the opportunity to peek behind the scenes to gain an understanding of the planning and desktop research that is essential before any successful dig can take place. In the case of understanding the wartime geography of the Lea Valley, Dave Hibbert of the GWAG geophysics team and the author spent a considerable amount of time researching and mapping the positions of the ring of defences that had been put in place to protect the north-eastern approaches to London. From the information gathered, Dave was able to produce some detailed maps which greatly improved our understanding of how the defence of London was arranged.

A great deal of the enemy action over Britain took place in the air space above the Lea Valley. This geographical region formed part of the London Air Defence Area (LADA). To deal with this new threat, several gun emplacements had been installed around the region and these were

Large Lea Valley map drawn by Dave Hibbert of GWAG showing gun emplacements, search light batteries, airfields and airship crash sites.

manned by gun crews from the Royal Artillery. These Anti Aircraft (AA) batteries had been put in place, along with searchlight batteries, to form a defensive shield around the capital to complement the work of the Royal Flying Corps who patrolled the sky above.

An aircraft that failed to land safely at Chingford Airfield, on the bank of King George V reservoir, 1915.

Two of the local gun emplacements, Monkhams Hall, Waltham Abbey and Pole Hill, Chingford, formed part of the Northern sector of LADA, an area comprising some eighteen guns. Invading Zeppelins, on a mission to bomb London, often came under attack from these guns as the airships made their way south, losing height, so that their observers could identify designated targets in the capital. Interestingly, when I researched the history of the Lea Valley Growers' Association, I did not discover any recorded incidents of growers encountering damage to their valuable glasshouses by the shock waves created by the guns as they blasted away at their leviathan targets.

Before taking television cameras to any of the potential dig sites it was decided to test the desktop research by carrying out an evaluation exercise on the site of the former Royal Naval Air Service (RNAS) airfield at Chingford. This was a difficult site to evaluate as, over the years, it had seen much disturbance and was now mainly covered by Thames Water's William Girling Reservoir. However, consulting site maps and old photographs during desktop research revealed that a narrow strip of land at the north end of the reservoir which was adjacent to the fence-line of the current Lea Valley Road (A110) had once contained a number of wooden huts. These would have probably been billets for the naval personnel who were involved with the operation of the airfield.

Before the archaeological team could get onto the airfield site the owner of a flock of sheep who had grazing rights on the Thames Water land had to be approached. Fortunately the man was very cooperative and moved his flock to another site so that the archaeological survey could begin. Dave Hibbert and Angie Cannon went to work straight away with their geophysics equipment to survey for evidence of underground structures. Unfortunately they were unable to obtain any results as the overhead electromagnetic radiation coming from a series of electricity pylons that ran across the site was so strong that it completely wiped out the geophysics readings.

As geophysics was now out of the question the archaeologists had to rely on a visual survey (mainly looking for unusual features in the landscape) and also the support from the metal-detectorists. The visual survey soon revealed that the main area of interest had recently been disturbed and it was learned that contractors for Thames Water had carried out work the previous week to put down a clinker path along the north side of the site. This was the area where the wooden huts were located on the early photograph. Amongst the rubble, disturbed by the contractors, were fragments of early 20th-century brickwork, some covered with bitumen that had clear impressions of wooden supports, a sort of archaeological finger print. From this evidence it was concluded that these bitumen-covered bricks would have formed the damp-proofed remains of brick peers on which the wooden huts would have once stood.

A number of test-pits were put in across various parts of the site but did not reveal any really exciting finds although the metal-detector team did discover a few metallic artefacts, including a 0.303 cartridge case, suggesting a link with the former airfield. As the archaeological team concluded that the airfield site had suffered too much disturbance over the years there was little point in spending more valuable time excavating. The test-pits were back-filled and the team left after just one day to be able to spend time on the next Lea Valley site which the desktop and preliminary field research suggested would be more promising.

The next site the GWAG undertook to survey was Monkhams Hall, a Great War gun emplacement that was positioned prominently on a hill to the east of the Crooked Mile and overlooking the town of Waltham Abbey, Essex. Most of the land surrounding the gun emplacement was currently in the ownership of the Corporation of London so permission had to be sought before a survey could take place. Fortunately the Corporation were extremely helpful and arrangements for the dig were put in place. However, once permission had been granted contractors had to be called in to cut the long grass which covered most of the dig site and also obscured some of the low-level remains of standing structures.

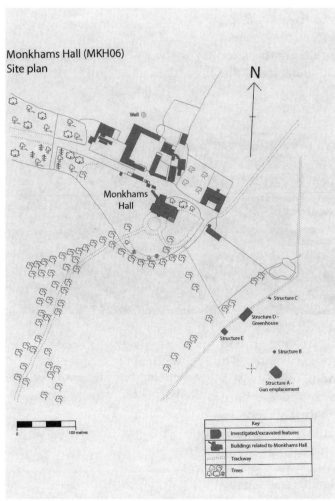

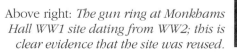

Monkhams Hall site plan.

Right: *The Monkhams Hall gun platform in the foreground with structure 'A' to the right, looking south.*

Above right: *The gun ring at Monkhams Hall WW1 site dating from WW2; this is clear evidence that the site was reused.*

The GWAG is made up of a team of volunteers consisting of both academic and professional archaeologists so there is little cash available to pay contractors to carry out the essential work of clearing a site prior to a dig commencing. Therefore, it was fortunate that BBC2 *Timewatch* wished to film the Monkhams Hall dig and the GWAG were given a small grant to pay for the grass cutting allowing the dig to start on time. However, the television schedule was very tight and this meant that the usual pre-excavation assessment that normally takes place before a dig, with a geophysics survey, had to be incorporated with the other archaeological activities of metal-detecting and the digging of test-pits during the television filming.

As it turned out this particular dig, despite having a team of eight working over five days, had not been able to establish a clear picture from the site excavation as the archaeology showed three different periods of occupation. First there was early evidence of a greenhouse and gardens which would have probably formed part of the Monkhams Hall estate. The second phase produced material evidence of a Great War gun emplacement which had already been identified by earlier desktop research. The third phase, which came as a surprise to the archaeologists, showed that the steel ring at the base of the Anti-Aircraft (AA) gun that allowed it to rotate to the required firing position was manufactured just before the Second World War. This strongly suggested that the gun emplacement had been re-occupied during this later conflict. Clearly more work would be needed to properly understand the different phases of occupation.

As mentioned earlier a considerable amount of the enemy action which occurred over Britain took place in the airspace above the Lea Valley. German airships on their way to attack London would normally make landfall on the Suffolk coast then make their way down country passing through Lea Valley airspace. The two local Anti Aircraft gun emplacements, Monkhams Hall and Pole Hill, Chingford were manned by gun crews from the Royal Artillery and, along with searchlight batteries, formed part of the defensive ring around London. This is why the Monkhams Hall site was chosen for excavation as it was felt the archaeology would improve our understanding of part of a militarised landscape that is little known and poorly recorded. We have probably recorded more and have a better understanding of the archaeology of ancient Egypt that we have about the militarised landscape of Britain that is only one hundred years old!

The Chingford Pole Hill gun emplacement, protecting London against incoming German aircraft during WW1.

Sometimes archaeology has an amusing side and the Monkhams Hall dig did not disappoint. Remember that we were digging a gun emplacement while television was filming and TV directors are normally looking for something exciting and spectacular that will engage their viewers. As the team of metal-detectorists were carrying out a site sweep, the TV director called 'find me a shell'! After a while one of the team got a massive signal on his equipment. Then, with trowel in hand, he began to slowly and carefully remove the soil to reveal the find. Suddenly a brass metal tip began to appear at the bottom of the freshly excavated trench. The author, who was observing the delicate removal of the soil, being an impatient man, called for a mattock then began taking out the earth above the object at a much faster pace. This caught the attention of the television director who appeared to turn a lighter shade of pale as he was convinced that an unexploded shell had been located which the author was about to set off at any moment! The order then came from the director to stop the dig immediately and a call was made to the Bomb Squad.

By seven o'clock that evening the Bomb Squad had not arrived and as I had a journey of over a hundred miles in front me I left the site in the capable hands of others. A week later I bumped into one of the archaeologists who had patiently waited for the arrival of the Bomb Squad and enquired 'Did they excavate the shell?' 'No,' he replied with a broad grin appearing across his face, 'it was an old table leg with a brass cap'! Who said archaeology was a dull and un-humorous subject?

Top soil being removed by mechanical digger and archaeologists at Theberton Hall Farm, Suffolk, crash site of Zeppelin L48.

REFERENCES

Durrani, Nadia & Faulkner, Neil *In Search of the Zeppelin War, the Archaeology of the First Blitz* (Tempus Publishing, Stroud, 2008)
Lewis, Jim, A personal account of the Great War Archaeology Group digs at the RNAS Chingford Airfield and Monkhams Hall sites in 2006

Note

May I take the opportunity to thank Dr Neil Faulkner, Dr Nadia Durrani, Dave Hibbert, and other members of the Great War Archaeology Group for providing maps and photographs for this section of the book.

9. THE ROYAL SMALL ARMS FACTORY, ENFIELD LOCK

In the early 19th century the government took the decision to build a small arms factory at Enfield Lock to relieve the state from having to rely on the private gun contractors, who were mainly situated in the London and Birmingham areas, for the supply of weapons for the British army and navy. Perhaps, not too unlike governments today, whose departments often seem incapable of efficiently overseeing major projects, the decision to have a state-controlled factory to manufacture quality weapons to fight Napoleon failed miserably. By 1816 the factory and the building of houses for the workforce had been completed but the Napoleonic Wars had ended in the previous year with Wellington's victory at the battle of Waterloo!

The next weapons organisational disaster for the government occurred in the middle of the 19th century when the factory was expanded to provide rifles for the British troops at the Crimea. During the war, when regiments at the front were screaming out for reliable weapons, the government decided to send a commission to the USA to see how the Americans were manufacturing rifles with interchangeable parts on a system of mass production. At the time in Britain individual parts of the rifle were filed to gauge by hand by skilled artisans and were not interchangeable. If a rifle part became damaged in battle the armourer had to make and individually fit the piece. Parts could not be taken off the shelf.

Eventually the Board of Ordnance placed orders for machine tools and gauges with American manufacturers; a new machine room was built at Enfield to take the imported machinery and an American foreman was hired to oversee the installation and help train the British workforce. The factory, now the Royal Small Arms Factory (RSAF) went into production in 1857 with the Enfield Pattern 1853 rifle. However, the war in the Crimea had ended the year before in 1856!

Almost one hundred years after being established and by the time of the Great War and with the factory still in state control, the RSAF appears to have learned some important lessons. By the turn of the century, and probably provoked by the success of the German designed Mauser rifle which the Boer marksmen had used to good effect against the British troops during the Anglo-Boer Wars, Enfield began to develop a range of small arms that were more efficient and accurate than their predecessors. This technological leap was also helped by the introduction of new and improved materials. To accommodate these changes it would suggest that the organisation of the factory had improved and if this were the case it might further suggest that government had adopted a less intrusive role in the running of the factory.

By 1895, after years of experiment with a range of different manufacturers' rifles, the Lee Enfield Mk I, which in its later guises was to become world famous, was born. In 1902 the short magazine, Lee Enfield (SMLE) bolt action MK I (0.303 inch calibre) was introduced into service. Between the years 1905 and 1907 Enfield developed four Marks of the SMLE. The MK III became the standard weapon adopted by the British Army and continued as the rifle of choice throughout the Great War. During the war the Enfield factory

The Short Magazine Lee Enfield No. 1 Mk. III.

The RSAF large machine room as it would have looked during the Great War.

RSAF Armourers second football team; the young men in uniform would suggest that the photo was taken c. 1914.

manufactured a staggering 2,007,119 rifles and bayonets and also produced large quantities of the Enfield MK II (0.45 inch calibre) revolver.

It is interesting to note that by the outbreak of the Great War the RSAF at Enfield had also designed a new rifle that fired a smaller high velocity round of 0.276 inch. However, with the production of the SMLE MK III, Enfield lacked the capacity to manufacture a new rifle and it was also felt that a weapon of smaller calibre should not be introduced alongside the standard 0.303 in time of war as confusion over ammunition supply and use could occur. This is precisely what happened at the time of the Crimean War when at least three different calibres of weapon were issued to the British forces. Perhaps government and the military hierarchy had finally learned another important lesson!

The design for the new weapon, now known as the Pattern 1914, was adapted to the standard 0.303 inch round and sent to manufacturing companies in

America where it was produced in its thousands. The Winchester factory produced 545,511 rifles, the Remington factory 545,541 and the Eddystone factory a staggering 1,181,908. However, due to slight differences between these manufacturers, presumably in the way machines were set up and also due to the fact that the Pattern 1914 was really a weapon in development rather than a drawing board design (fully dimensioned engineering drawings did not exist) this meant that components between the three factories were not one hundred percent interchangeable.

When the American army entered the Great War in April 1917 the Pattern 1914 was modified by the US Ordnance Department and chambered for the standard US 30-60 bullet, becoming known as Model 1917, sometimes called the M1917 Enfield. Production of the weapon was carried out by the same three manufacturers that produced the Pattern 1914. The scale of production was such that it overtook the quantities produced by the Springfield Armoury. Springfield was a supplier of the standard weapon to the American forces. By the end of the Great War it was estimated that around seventy-five percent of American soldiers in Europe were equipped with the M1917, a figure which no doubt made the RSAF development engineers exceedingly proud of their achievements.

American soldier posing in a studio with a M 1917 Enfield, probably manufactured in the USA by Remington.

While the large number of weapons produced at Enfield during the Great War may at first seem surprising, considering the factory's past record under the Board of Ordnance, research in the 1990s by Professor Tim Putnam and Dr Dan Weinbren of Middlesex University suggest that by the start of hostilities things had dramatically changed at the factory when they wrote:

> *Overtime working began immediately and crews for twelve hour day and night shifts were set up before the end of the month, to work from six to six. From 2nd September day shift men worked on Sundays from 7:30 to 5:30. Soon a thirteen day fortnight became compulsory. Factory Act constraints on the working time of boys were suspended until August 1916. Boys under 16 were restricted to a 60 hour week and others to 65 and boys working overtime excluded from night shift.*

At the time of researching the Great War stories for this chapter an RSAF mystery has come to light which has raised a number of questions, answers to which have yet to found.

In 1911 an American Army Colonel, Isaac Newton Lewis designed a light machine gun that became known as the Lewis gun. The weapon was adopted by the Allies and was manufactured under licence in Britain by the Birmingham Small Arms Company (BSA). It was also produced on the continent for the Belgian Army by manufacturers in Liege. Both

Photo of mainly women canteen staff at RSAF c. 1918.

RSAF Officers and technical staff 7 December 1918.

the Belgian and British versions of the weapon were built to accept the standard 0.303 inch British round. There were two models of the Lewis gun, one with a magazine holding forty-seven rounds and an aircraft version with a ninety-seven round magazine. The gun was a favourite with the Royal Flying Corps as it only weighed 12kg and was lighter than the Vickers machine gun. Also, the gun being air-cooled made it ideal as an aircraft weapon. Removing the gun's cooling jacket and fins when installing it in an aircraft reduced the overall weight of the weapon by a further 3kg.

Australian members of the Machine Gun Corps training with Lewis Guns, probably in Belton Park, Grantham, Lincolnshire.

Lewis guns being assembled at the Royal Small Arms Factory.

The mystery comes from three different photographs of Lewis guns which all appear to have been taken around the same time in what seems to be an assembly shop at the Royal Small Arms Factory. Ray Tuthill, a former engineer at the RSAF and a member of the RSAF Apprentices Association has, after considerable detective work, identified the assembly shop as a building that was once situated at the north end of the Enfield factory site. We also have evidence that the Lewis guns in question are aircraft versions. They were identified as such by the late Herbert Woodend MBE (Bert or Herbie to his friends) an internationally acknowledged weapons expert who was once in charge of both the Enfield and Nottingham Pattern Rooms. He has written the details and added his signature to the back of one of the photographs.

Lewis Gun assembly at the Royal Small Arms Factory.

Another view of Lewis Guns being assembled in a different shop at the Royal Small Arms Factory.

To date no documentary material has come to light that suggests the RSAF were 'manufacturing' Lewis guns during the period of the Great War but it would appear, from the photographic evidence, that they were certainly assembling the weapons in a building on the Enfield site. If this is the case it is likely that a contract existed (or exists), perhaps with the Birmingham Small Arms Company. Therefore, as the author is on a tight deadline, may I appeal to any budding Sherlock Holmes out there to help solve the Lewis gun mystery?

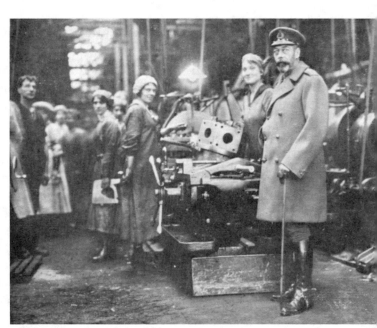

This picture has a caption 'King George V at the Royal Small Arms 1915'. However it is possible the King is visiting the Ponders End Shell Works in 1917.

A front-mounted aircraft Lewis Gun.

REFERENCES

Lewis, Jim, *From Gunpowder to Guns the Story of Two Lea Valley Armouries* (Middlesex University Press, London, 2009)

Putnam, Tim & Weinbren, Dan, *A Short History of the Royal Small Arms Factory Enfield* (Centre for Applied Historical Studies, Middlesex University, 1992)

Skennerton, Ian D., *The Lee Enfield Story* (Ian D. Skennerton, Australia, 1993)

Personal conversations with Ray Tuthill (former RSAF engineer) and Glen Chapelle (curator of Royal Ordnance archive, BAE Systems, Glascoed), December 2013

Note

During the Great War the RSAF, Enfield was responsible for repairing large quantities of Vickers Machine Guns.

Note 2

I should like to give my sincere thanks to Ray Tuthill, former Treasurer of the RSAF Apprentices Association, and Patrick Gray, of the RSA Trust, for their help and advice when writing this chapter.

10. ELEY BROTHERS FACTORY, EDMONTON

Today it would be hard to imagine that at the time of the Great War the region of the Lea Valley which has now become the London Borough of Enfield, was home to a number of prominent arms and explosives manufacturers.

In the 1820s, the brothers William and Charles Eley took a small factory in Charlotte Street, London to progress the ideas of William, a silversmith by trade, for making gun cartridges. Later the brothers moved to Emmett's Mews, off Old Bond Street and were known as Eley and Company, becoming acknowledged as cartridge and percussion cap manufacturers. In 1828 their first real commercial venture was to produce a 'wire cartridge' from a patent that they had bought from a Joshua Jenour. The idea behind this cartridge design was a method which contained the lead shot within a wire frame during the early stages of flight. This reduced the spread of pellets during trajectory.

By all accounts the initial sales of the Eley 'wire cartridge' did not go terribly well and Charles, who appears to have been the business's main financial supporter, left the company. During the 1830s William improved the design of the 'wire cartridge' and added percussion caps to his product range and these changes seem to have improved the viability of the business.

In 1841, tragedy struck the Eley business when William was killed in an explosion. An article in *The Times*, Monday 28th June 1841 reported the gory details of William's death thus '… he was surrounded by a quantity of dark-coloured blood, his left arm and hand were blown off, his right thigh was nearly severed, both his feet were blown to atoms, his person in other respects was mutilated and blackened and scarcely a remnant of his apparel was left about him'. At the hearing at the Westminster Coroner's Court, the evidence given by his brother Charles, a resident of Cheshunt, stated 'the deceased was in the habit of using detonating or fulminating mercury, a composition of a most combustible and dangerous nature'. Charles also informed the Court that he was in no doubt that William had been stirring the composition when it exploded. *The Times* had reported that the explosion occurred on 'Friday evening [25th June], between the hours of 6 and 7 o'clock' and although the building suffered extensive damage there were no other injuries mentioned by the newspaper. This probably indicates that William Eley was working alone on that fateful evening.

The business was taken over by William's three sons who appear to have been quite go-ahead people as evidenced by moves to larger premises in 1851 and 1859. In 1855, the eldest son William Thomas, had helped Samuel Colt, the famous American arms manufacturer, develop a special cartridge for his revolvers (Colt had established a factory at Pimlico, London after exhibiting at the Great Exhibition of 1851).

Following a move to Grays Inn Road, London in 1864 the company became involved with the development of Colonel Boxer's cartridge. This was a metal cased cartridge which contained black power ignited by a 'centre fire' percussion cap that could be removed, making it possible to recycle the metallic case. These cartridges were eventually adopted by the British Government and Eley's received large orders. Vast quantities of the cartridge were also made by other manufacturers, becoming standard issue for British troops.

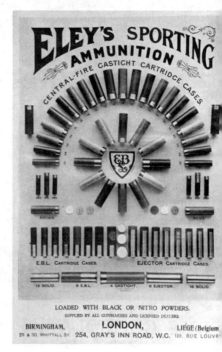

Early advertisement for Eley Brothers cartridges.

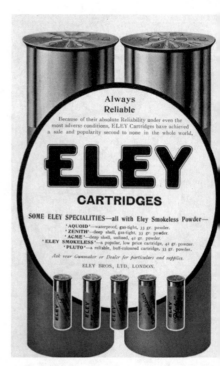

Eley Brothers advertisement claiming reliability for their cartridges.

By 1865 Eleys had moved into the Lea Valley and established a factory at Tile Kiln Lane Edmonton. The move appears timely as the 1870s saw demand for rifle ammunition increase dramatically as many countries around the world began adopting the new breech-loading weapons as the old muzzle-loader had effectively become obsolete.

However, the increase in breech-loading weapons had a down-side for the cartridge-making industry as different rifle manufactures continued to make their weapons with different calibre barrels. This put considerable pressure on manufacturers like Eley Brothers, who at the time, tended to rely on labour intensive methods of production. In 1874, to help take advantage of the new business opportunities that were occurring Eley Brothers opted to become a public liability company (Eley Brothers Limited) with a capital of £200,000, improving their financial position. The diversity of ammunition can be gauged in their 1890s trade catalogues where over one thousand products are listed, included four hundred different types of cartridges. In the manufacturing experience of the author, having such a large and diverse product range creates a quality assurance nightmare and usually results in serious financial problems for the business.

In 1903 the company moved to a new factory complex on the north side of Angel Road, Edmonton (now the North Circular Road the A 406), located between the railway line and Salmon's Brook. The move caused delays in cartridge production and when quantities of 0.303 ammunition were returned to the factory with split cases, the War Office took Eley Brothers off the Approved List of Suppliers. In 1907 Eley's approached the War Office and asked to be put back on the approved supplier list but before this could be considered, the War Office sent an inspection team to the Edmonton factory, who were less than happy with what they found. The team was particularly critical with regard to the scant level of laboratory equipment and also the lack of a comprehensive quality assessment plan for the company's products. However, on condition that Eley's put in place certain War Office recommendations they were put back on the approved supplier list. After this particular embarrassing scare one would have expected that Eley's would have paid considerable attention to all aspects of production detail; but apparently not. In 1909 the company was again removed from the War Office list when again 0.303 ammunition, was found to have suffered from split cases in storage. This was put down to poor standards of cartridge annealing which was not carried out scientifically. The procedure had been to place cartridge cases in trays in a furnace and their readiness was judged by eye, leaving most in a brittle state.

This second rejection by the War Office appears to have finally acted as a wake-up call to the company. They now secured the exclusive services of F W Jones, a chemist and leading ballistics expert who oversaw the loading of all samples that were to be sent to the London and Birmingham Proof Houses. Also, in 1910, two small companies were purchased that could provide shot and improved smokeless powders which meant that Eley's had a better control of their supply chain.

By the time of the Great War Eley Brothers had considerably improved the quality of its product and also had enhanced its commercial image and was again receiving War Office contracts for 0.303 ammunition. As more fighter aircraft were built to engage the Zeppelins that had begun bombing attacks over Britain a new type of incendiary ammunition was required to be mixed

Eley Brothers ammunition list early 20th century.

with the standard 0.303 round in the magazines of Royal Flying Corps Lewis guns. This was to ignite the escaping hydrogen from these gigantic airships after the standard round had penetrated a Zeppelin's gas bags. One of the types of incendiary ammunition used was named 'Pomeroy', after its inventor, and Eley's turned these cartridges out in quantity.

A paper published in 1909 by the Explosives Section of the 7th International Congress of Applied Chemistry lists Eley' Brothers' Edmonton site as consisting of sixty acres on which are 'Five main buildings in which manufacture is carried on. Four magazines and a number of isolated wooden buildings specially arranged to meet the requirements of the Explosives Act'. It is probably fair to conclude that due to the size and facilities offered by the site Eley's were given responsibility for other munitions work, including the filling of rifle and hand grenades. Also they were asked by government to erect and manage a Government Cartridge Factory (G.C.F.4) to increase the supply of small arms ammunition to aid the war effort. In this new facility 7.62mm ammunition was manufactured for the Russian Government. However, after the Russian Revolution in October 1917 production of the 7.62mm ammunition ceased and the factory went over to repairing aircraft engines.

By the end of the Great War the government took the decision to rationalise the ammunition and explosives industry which at the time consisted of some seventeen British companies. In November 1918, after the declaration of peace, an umbrella organisation was formed called the Explosives Trades Limited and Eley's became part of this grouping. The largest organisation within the alliance was Nobel Explosives Limited and in 1919 Explosives Trades Limited became Nobel Industries.

In 1921 Eley Brothers' Edmonton factory closed and all production was transferred to Nobel's factory at Waltham Abbey, Essex. The following year Nobel Industries were appointed sole directors of the board which meant control passed to their hands and Eley's had no say in the running of what remained of their company. Within two years their metallic cartridge plant at Waltham Abbey was closed and production transferred to Knoch in

The name Eley has been captured in the Eley Industrial Estate situated on the north side of the A406 in the London Borough of Enfield.

Eley Brothers shot tower, looking north from Nobel Road, 1960.

Right: *Close up view of top section of Eley Brothers shot tower under demolition 1991.*

Far right: *Eley Brothers shot tower under demolition, 1991.*

Birmingham; part of the Nobel empire. In 1926 Nobel Industries became part of the even larger Imperial Chemical Industries (ICI) and in the same year the remaining Eley's production was transferred from Waltham Abbey to Knoch's Birmingham factory.

In 1928, one hundred years after Eley's had been founded, the company went into liquidation although the brand name remains to this day. During the Great War the Edmonton factory manufactured some two hundred and nine million 0.303 cartridges and carried out other work in support of the Allied Forces. While the figures might sound impressive, other large ammunition manufacturers had produced over ten times this amount. This was because they had invested in modern machinery and also carried out most of the work associated with the manufacture of cartridge components in-house, rather than rely on outside contractors. In-house working meant issues of quality and tolerance could quickly be solved.

Eley's, on the other hand, had been slow to invest as heavily as others in new machinery and had, over the years, relied too much on external contractors for cartridge components and other processes. Nevertheless, it would be hard to imagine that Eley Brothers' contribution to the Great War did not play a significant part in the overall outcome, not just in the amount and variety of ammunition that was manufactured but also in the improvements they had introduced to the design of the 0.303 cartridge.

REFERENCES

Author unknown, *The Rise and Progress of the British Explosives Industry* (Published under the auspices of the VII International Congress of Applied Chemistry by its Explosives Section, London, 1909)

Author unknown, Dreadful Explosion in Old Bond Street (*The Times*, 28 June 1841)

Pople-Crump, John, The British Ammunition Trade, Eley Brothers *(1828 – 1928)* (*Guns Review* vol.22, no.3, March 1982)

11. THE PONDERS END SHELL WORKS

David Lloyd George, when discussing Britain's preparedness for the production of explosives, wrote in his memoirs that; 'At the outbreak of the War, State production was limited to the Royal Gunpowder Factory at Waltham Abbey, which made about 75 short tons (i.e., 150,000 lb.) of cordite and gunpowder a week.' This was clearly not enough to supply the needs of the Allies at the front. This general lack of high explosive shells had probably encouraged the Commander-in-chief of the British Expeditionary Force (1914–1915), Field Marshall Sir John French, to take the extraordinary step of giving an interview to *The Times* on 27 March where he called for more ammunition. A few days earlier French had been rebuked by the King for giving an interview to the French news agency, *Havas*. These remarkable revelations by such a high-ranking officer would suggest that the Great War was now being fought on a political front. The criticisms by the military and also the pressure from the Northcliffe Press (owners of *The Times* and *Daily Mail*) sparked high level debates in Parliament which eventually culminated in the formation of a Coalition Government (between Liberal party and Unionist /Conservative party) and the appointment of Lloyd George as Minister of Munitions. Later Lloyd George would become Prime Minister, with support from the Conservatives, after a minority second Coalition Government was formed.

Belgian refugees working in a shell factory during WW1.

Ponders End Shell Works, Women's canteen 1916.

Munitions at Ponders End Shell Works.

The machine shop at the Ponders End Shell Works.

Winston Churchill gives a speech at the Ponders End Shell Works, 1916.

In 1915 a shell factory was set up on the south side of Wharf Road, Ponders End with government providing eighty percent of the capital expenditure amounting to £80,000 and a further £137,000 as working capital. The private company that took on the task of shell production at Ponders End was the Reece Roturbo Manufacturing Company Limited of Wolverhampton. This company specialised in the manufacture of centrifugal and other pumps and was classified as iron workers, founders, smelters, smiths, engineers and ironmasters. Having such an industrial background would suggest that this company lacked experience in the manufacture of munitions. However, many factories who had effectively become part of the wartime State manufacturing industry through government control, under the introduction of the Defence

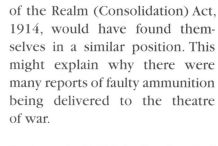

of the Realm (Consolidation) Act, 1914, would have found themselves in a similar position. This might explain why there were many reports of faulty ammunition being delivered to the theatre of war.

By the end of 1915 the Ponders End Shell Factory had produced and shipped almost fifty thousand eight-inch shells. The following year Lloyd George and Winston Churchill separately visited the factory which by now had expanded production and was producing six-inch and eight-inch shells and also shells for heavy howitzers (usually described as a gun that could fire shells with high trajectories).

Some years ago I had a conversation about the Ponders End Shell Works with the late Graham Dalling, the very knowledgeable Enfield local historian and archivist. I recall Graham mentioning a rumour he had once heard that during the Great War the Ponders Shell Works had produced chemical weapons. When writing this chapter the chemical weapons story emerged from the depths of my brain and I pondered if there could be some substance in this planted thought? I began to look for any evidence that might have prompted the story.

During the third battle of Gaza in 1917 it is known that General Edmund Allenby's army fired some ten thousand missiles filled with poisonous gas at enemy positions. It is also known that, at the time, the scientists at the government laboratories at Porton Down, Wiltshire had developed an exploding shell, the 'M Device', which was capable of delivering highly toxic gas. Major General Charles Foulks, who was in charge of the 'M Device' development, suggested that it was 'the most effective chemical weapon ever devised'.

In assessing the evidence available, we know from recent research by *The Guardian*, that Winston Churchill, who became Minister of Munitions after David Lloyd George, was a powerful advocate for the use of chemical weapons and, as mentioned above, he did visit the Ponders End Shell Works. On the battlefield toxic chemicals are usually delivered by bombs or shells, so was it possible that the Ponders End Shell Works was actually manufacturing the delivery vehicle for this abhorrent material? If this was the case, and we will probably never know the whole truth, it could account for the rumour passed to me by Graham Dalling.

Although the post-war cabinet was against Churchill's enthusiasm for the use of chemical weapons somehow they seemed powerless to prevent their deployment. In August 1919, according to a recent article in *The Guardian*, British aircraft began dropping missiles filled with poisonous gas on Bolshevik held villages in Russia. It is estimated that during the attempted repression of the Bolshevik uprising an astonishing fifty thousand 'M Devices' were sent to Russia; a cruel reflection of man's inhumanity to man which, with regard to the current crisis in Syria, never seems to have diminished.

Above left: *A battery of Livings gas projectors being loaded by Royal Engineers for testing at Porton Down.*

Above right: *Women stand beside range of shells demonstrating the size of these lethal projectiles.*

George V at the Ponders End Shell Works, 1917.

George V's visit to Ponders End Shell Works, March 1917.

REFERENCES

Lloyd George, David, *War Memoirs*, vol. 2 (Odhams Press Limited, Watford 1933)

Massey, William Thomas, *How Jerusalem was Won: Being the Record of Allenby's Campaign in Palestine* (Constable & Company, London, 1919)

Pam, David, *A History of Enfield 1914-1939: a desirable neighbourhood*, Vol.3 (Enfield Preservation Society (Enfield 1990)

World News, Winston Churchill's shocking use of chemical weapons (*The Guardian*, London, 1/09/2013)

12. JACOB COHEN THE FOUNDER OF A FOOD EMPIRE

Jacob Cohen was born on 29 October 1898 into a poor emigrant family from Poland who had settled in Whitechapel, in London's east end. His father, Avrom a tailor by trade, worked in the sweatshops of London. After long hours, much sacrifice and watching every penny, Avrom was able save sufficient money to move his family to an address in Hackney where he set up as a jobbing tailor.

Young Jacob entered school at the age of six and, like many children of his generation, left education when he was fourteen. Also, like many of his peers, his school reports often contained passages like 'must try harder' and 'lacks application'. The years running up to the Great War were hard for the population of London's east end and opportunities for betterment were slim. Work for the average person, if they were lucky enough to get it, normally consisted of long hours and low pay with little prospect for improvement. Jacob's first job was with his brother-in-law, Morris Israel, in the street markets of London. After a short spell with Morris he left and went to work at his father's tailoring

A young Jack Cohen after becoming Air Mechanic second-class (number 64535).

business. Here he worked long hours into the night sewing buttonholes into jackets for which he received only pocket money. As one might imagine Jacob hated the job and looked for the chance to escape. In March 1917, at the age of eighteen, the opportunity eventually came and Jacob joined the Royal Flying Corps (RFC) where he trained as an air mechanic. During his period of training Jacob suffered racial abuse and he reluctantly allowed himself to be known as Jack rather than Jacob to escape his tormentors.

Jack's first posting was to the Balloon Training Wing at Roehampton where he worked as a rigger before being sent to the Middle East. When Jack's troopship was entering Alexandria harbour it was torpedoed by an enemy submarine and Jack, a non-swimmer, almost drowned. Fortunately he survived the incident and the rest of his service career turned out to be less eventful.

Advertisement for Royal Flying Corps personnel WW1.

On demobilisation from the RFC in 1919, Jack, like many other ex-servicemen, who had bravely served their country, was rewarded with unemployment, a fate that did not suit his character. Although his father had wanted him to return to his tailoring business Jack did not wish to give up his new-found freedoms that easily. With few civilian skills to offer a potential employer Jack's mind drifted back to the street markets of London when he had worked for his brother-in-law Morris Israel. Now with a thirty pound demobilisation gratuity, Jack hired a street barrow and invested the remainder in a quantity of ex-NAAFI (Navy, Army and Air Force Institutes) foodstuffs. These had probably come onto the market after the war as the NAAFI reduced wartime stocks.

Observati
balloon W

Right: *Aerial photograph taken from a tethered balloon.*

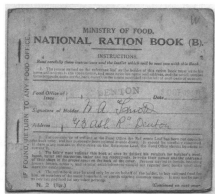

Far right:*National ration book issued during WW1.*

With a barrow load of goods, Jack made his way to Well Street, in London's east end, where he was able to rent part of a market site from an established trader. In his first day of trading Jack sold £4-worth of groceries of which twenty-five percent (£1) was profit. Jack seems to have been blessed with an entrepreneurial spirit as he soon mastered the 'show business' way of the other traders, selling tinned milk, not at three-pence, not at two-pence – it's yours for a penny. Other foodstuffs like golden syrup, broken biscuits, tinned jam etc., were sold in a similar way to his working-class customers who were always on the lookout for a bargain. Jack learned very quickly that, in the harsh reality of east-end life, low prices were crucial to the growing success of his little enterprise. Within six months of pushing his barrow to Well Street Market, Jack was trading in at least two other east-end markets. Now it would seem that Jack had found his true vocation and was destined for greater things. According to David Powell, Jack's biographer, 'he had become not only a tradesman but also an entertainer'.

Well Street market, Hackney where Jack Cohen began selling NAAFI surplus goods after WW1.

The next few years were quite eventful for Jack. He moved stock that he had been keeping in his father's house to a small lock-up premises that he had acquired in Clarence Road, Clapton. Here he piled his ever-increasing wares high until larger premises were found nearby in Upper Clapton Road. In 1920 Jack opened an account with the Midland Bank in Hackney as the takings from one of his stalls in the Caledonian Market had exceeded one hundred pounds in a single day. After only two years of trading Jack was operating from around six London markets and he had also established himself as a supplier of groceries to other traders.

In January 1924 Jack found time to marry his sweetheart Sarah (Cissie) Fox, and her five-hundred pound dowry, along with one hundred and thirty pounds in wedding gifts, was wisely deposited in a Post Office savings account. A house was rented in Gore Road, Hackney and it was there that their two children were born, Irene in 1926 and Shirley in 1930. Later, in 1924, Jack would take on new business that would prove to be a lasting legacy to his entrepreneurial skills.

Always on the lookout for new buying and selling opportunities in the food trade, Jack met T E Stockwell, a partner in the tea-importing firm of Torring and Stockwell. Jack arranged to buy tea from the company in bulk at nine old

Tesco House, Cheshunt headquarters of Jack Cohen's food empire.

pennies per pound and then sell it on in half pound packs at six old pennies, a mark-up of thirty-three percent. Interestingly, Jack established a brand name for the tea by combining the first two initials of his supplier with the first two letters of his second name Cohen, making the now famous name of one of the world's leading grocers and household goods suppliers; TESCO.

Would any of today's customers entering a TESCO store anywhere in the world remotely appreciate that this thriving international business was created by an ex-serviceman from the Great War who had invested his thirty pounds gratuity to buy a job-lot of surplus NAAFI food?

Sir John (Jack) Cohen (1898–1979).

REFERENCES

Lewis, Jim, *From Eton Manor to the Olympics, More Lea Valley Secrets Revealed* (Libri Publishing Limited, Oxford, 2010)

Powell, David, *Counter Revolution, the Tesco Story* (Grafton Books, London, 1991)

Note

In 1969 Jack Cohen was knighted for his services to retailing, becoming Sir John Cohen.

13. THE TANK AND VIRGIN QUEEN SHARE COMMON GROUND!

Who might have guessed that the County of Hertfordshire holds a unique place in the winning of the Great War and, unlikely as it may seem, that is due to one of Britain's historic buildings – Hatfield House and grounds?

Hatfield House and grounds.

Below left: *A young Queen Elizabeth 1.*

Below right: *Sir Robert Cecil, 1st Earl of Salisbury.*

The present Hatfield House, which has the River Lea meandering through the estate, was built in 1611 for Robert Cecil, First Earl of Salisbury. Cecil held a powerful position in the governance of England as a trusted Chief Minister to King James I. Within the grounds of Hatfield House stand part of the old wing of the Royal Palace of Hatfield, built in 1497, under the supervision of Henry VII's Lord Chancellor, Cardinal John Morton.

In the reign of Henry VIII the palace was claimed by the King and this was where two of his children, King Edward VI and the future Queen Elizabeth I spent their formative years. The story goes that on 17 November 1558, when sitting under an oak tree in the grounds of the Hatfield estate, the young Princess Elizabeth received the news that her sister Queen Mary had died and she had acceded to the throne. Three days later, on 20 November, Elizabeth held her first Council of State in the Great Hall at Hatfield Palace where she appointed William Cecil (who became Lord Burghley in 1571) to be her Privy Councillor. Cecil became Elizabeth's most trusted aide throughout her reign of almost forty-five years. When James I came to the throne in 1603 Robert Cecil (son of William), who had formerly been

Secretary of State under Elizabeth, carried on the role under James. In 1607 James and Cecil swapped estates, James taking over Cecil's Theobalds Palace and Cecil acquiring the Hatfield estate.

Wind the clock forward to the year 1915 when trials of a secret vehicle, designed by Major Walter Gordon Wilson and Sir William Ashbee Triton, and built by William Foster & Co. Ltd., at their small factory in Lincoln, started. Early trials of the vehicle had begun at various sites including Lincoln's Burton Park (now no longer there). However, having trials in public places of a prototype vehicle gave rise to serious concerns about keeping the project secret.

Early in 1916, the Fourth Marquess of Salisbury, James Edward Hubert Gascoyne Cecil, came to the rescue of the project when he gave over the grounds of Hatfield House to allow trials of this new vehicle, the world's first fighting tank, to take place in greater seclusion. Before the tanks arrived, and to make the trials authentic, part of the Hatfield estate was turned into a mini-Western Front, when craters and trenches were dug and coils of barbed-wire were laid.

Sir William Cecil, 1st Baron Burghley.

One night in late January 1916, under the cover of darkness, tanks were loaded onto a train at Lincoln's St. Marks Railway Station and covered over for security before being transported to Hatfield for the first series of serious trials. On 2 February 1916 the second series of trials began this time in front of a rather prestigious audience including David Lloyd George, then Minister of Munitions, Lord Kitchener, Secretary of State for War and the former Prime Minister, Arthur James Balfour, then First Lord of the Admiralty. The group also included some high-ranking military officers. The Hatfield tank trials were reported to have gone well although Lord Kitchener did not appear to be

A football team of men of Special Brigade, Royal Engineers, Hatfield Park, 1916.

particularly enthusiastic about the tank as a fighting vehicle, suggesting that they were 'a pretty mechanical toy'. In spite of Kitchener's comments, and due to the intervention of King George V who had arrived at Hatfield on 8 February to see further trials, orders were placed for the tank. By September 1916 tanks had entered the conflict on the Western Front at Flers-Courcelette, part of the Battle on the Somme. This was the first time in history that tanks had been deployed in warfare.

"A" Company, 14 Battalion Hertfordshire Home Guard, in front of Big Willie, Hatfield Park, 1944.

A young boy admires Big Willie in Hatfield Park.

Big Willie on trials in Hatfield Park, 1916.

The timely intervention of King George V is interesting as during the war years, the King travelled the country visiting factories and shipyards and took the opportunity of talking to both management and workers with a view to boosting morale and encouraging the workforce to maintain their efforts in supplying the Allies. There are photographs of George V visiting industries in the Lea Valley region including the Royal Gunpowder Mills, Waltham Abbey, the Royal Small Arms Factory, Enfield Lock, and the Ponders End Shell Works, Enfield.

At the end of the war, in 1919, Winston Churchill, Secretary of State for War and Secretary of State for Air, presented a Mark 1 tank to the 4th Marquess of Salisbury in recognition for the use of the Hatfield estate as a tank proving ground. Here the tank stood on display, providing a regular source of

Mark 1 tank (Big Willie) in Hatfield Park where it remained until the 1970s.

enjoyment to several generations of children visiting the park. In the 1970s, after becoming somewhat dishevelled and vandalised, the tank was moved to the Bovington Tank Museum where it was restored and put on display.

In 2014, four hundred and fifty-four years after Princess Elizabeth heard the news that she was now Queen of England, in the grounds of what is now Hatfield House, we honour the memory of those who gave their lives in the Great War (1914–1918). Perhaps we should also take time to reflect upon another remarkable event that took place in the grounds of Hatfield House ninety-eight years ago, in 1916, which probably helped the Allies in shortening the conflict!

REFERENCES

Glanfield, John, *Devil's Chariots: the birth and secret battles of the first tanks* (Sutton Publishing Limited, Stroud, 2001)

Liddle Hart, B.H, *The History of the World War 1914-1918* (Faber and Faber Limited, London, 1934)

Lloyd George, David, *War Memoirs*, Vol. 2 (Odhams Press Limited, Watford, 1933)

Matthew, H.C.G. and Harrison, Brian, *Oxford Dictionary of National Biography* (Oxford University Press, Oxford, 2004)

Pullen, Richard, *The Landships of Lincoln* (Tucann Books, Lincoln 2003)

Note

There are a number of stories and theories of how the name 'tank' came about. However, it is generally accepted that when the vehicle was first built it looked like a water-tank. It is also suggested that the workers at William Foster & Co. were told, when constructing the vehicles, that they were building mobile water-tanks for use in warfare in the deserts of Mesopotamia. This was done to reduce the risk of stories leaking out in the interests of security.

The tanks which first took part in the Hatfield trials were named 'Little Willie' (the first prototype) and 'Big Willie', the latter becoming known as 'Mother', because she gave birth to the various Marks that came later. Those tanks that were equipped with projecting cannon (typically six-pounders) were classified as 'male' and those without, 'female'.

Note 2

Robert Cecil's former home, Theobalds Palace, was located in Cheshunt a few miles from Hatfield House. Little remains of the palace today but small traces of the building can be found in Cedars Park.

Note 3

Can I take this opportunity to thank Rosemary Lee-Bapty of the Mill Green Museum and Mill, Hatfield for allowing the author to use the museum's research room on a day when the facility was officially closed. Such cooperation is rare.

14. OTHER LEA VALLEY CONTRIBUTORS TO THE GREAT WAR

Many factories and other establishments within the Lea Valley made significant contributions to the war effort, not all within the realms of the military or weapons making. For example Wright's Mill at Ponders End not only provided flour for a civilian population, but also for the army on the Western Front. Factories such as Fullers of Walthamstow, who manufactured a range of electric motors for industry, had to increase output as other manufacturers required these devices to drive their war-hungry machinery. To list every Lea Valley industry and institution that played a part in supporting the Great War would be an almost impossible task and well beyond the author's remit. However, the opportunity will be taken to record some of the little-known stories so that the history of the period is not entirely lost.

The Thames Ironworks, Canning Town

The Thames Ironworks at Canning Town in the Lower Lea Valley began life as Ditchburn and Mare in the early 1840s. Initially the shipyard was located on the west bank of the River Lea in the county of Middlesex, close to where the river enters the Thames.

By the mid-1840s the yard was having difficulties acquiring regular supplies of iron at competitive rates and Mare suggested to his partner that they should consider manufacturing their own iron plate. Ditchburn was not sympathetic to the suggestion and the partnership dissolved.

Thames Ironworks building and yard, Canning Town.

In 1846 Mare acquired land on the east bank of the River Lea in the county of Essex and set up as C J Mare & Company manufacturing a range of ships in both iron and wood. By the time of the Crimean War in 1853 the yard was receiving orders from both the British Admiralty and the French Government. Unfortunately the increase in war work appears to have pushed Mare into financial difficulty and the company was finally taken over by Peter Rolt, Mare's father-in-law. In 1857, under the chairmanship of Rolt, the company became the Thames Ironworks & Shipbuilding Co.

HMS Albion launched in 1898; during WW 1 she was involved in several different operations including the Dardanelles Campaign in 1915.

In 1910 the yard received an order from the British Admiralty to build *HMS Thunderer*, the largest battleship ever to be built on the Thames, weighing in excess of twenty-two thousand tons and costing just under two million pounds. When the ship was commissioned in 1912 *Thunderer*'s armament consisted of ten 13.5 inch guns mounted in five twin turrets and sixteen 4-inch guns. She was also fitted with the latest Marconi wireless system. In May 1916 *Thunderer* fought at the Battle of Jutland sustaining no damage.

Sadly *Thunderer* was the last ship to be built at the Thames Ironworks and the yard closed through lack of orders, laying off a skilled workforce. Prior to closure, Winston Churchill then First Lord of the Admiralty had been

HMS Thunderer, the last ship to be built at the Thames Ironworks in 1911; she went on to fight at the battle of Jutland.

petitioned by Thames Ironworks' management for further orders but their pleas were unsuccessful. At the time Germany was building up its High Seas Fleet and it was obvious to most people that war was only months away. Under the circumstances one would have expected that ways could have been found to keep the yard open as conflict was looming on the horizon. It would appear that government had been foolhardy in the extreme not to have retained the services of a shipyard that had accrued seventy years of marine skills and know-how that could have been put to good use even before hostilities commenced.

REFERENCES

Bradbury, Philip, *Shipbuilders of the Thames and Medway*, David and Charles, (Newton Abbott 1971)

Lewis, Jim, *London's Lea Valley, Britain's Best Kept Secret* (Phillimore & Company Limited, Chichester, 1999)

Mackrow, G.C., Some Reminiscences of the Early Days of the Thames Iron Works and Shipbuilding Company (*Thames Ironworks Gazette*, vol.1, 1895)

Mackrow, G.C., Some Reminiscences of the Early Days of the Thames Iron Works and Shipbuilding Company (*Thames Ironworks Gazette*, vol.2, 1896)

Powell, W.R. (ed.), *West Ham 1886 – 1986* (Council of the London Borough of Newham, 1986)

The Associated Equipment Company (AEC), Walthamstow

An AEC 'Y' Type truck with a very relaxed looking driver, cigarette in hand.

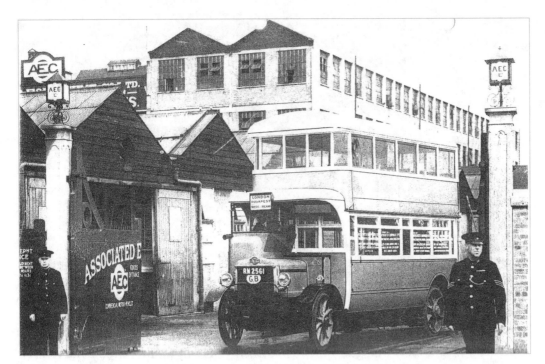

An AEC bus leaving the gates of the Walthamstow factory.

In January 1905, from a small rented tin hut in Hookers Lane, Walthamstow, Arthur Salisbury-Jones, a member of the Stock Exchange, launched the London Motor Omnibus Construction Company. Jones had wanted to manufacture reliable standardised motor buses to serve London commuters, who up until then had put up with a transport system that mainly relied on 'horse-power'. If Jones's plan for London proved successful then his grand vision was to roll out the scheme across the country.

By October 1910, and after much factory expansion, Jones launched the 'B'-type bus, a vehicle that was to become renowned for its excellent reliability. From a production rate of three 'B'-types per week the figure reached fifty per week some eighteen months later. In June 1912, due to structural changes taking place, the London Motor Omnibus Construction Company became the now more familiar Associated Equipment Company Limited (AEC).

Shortly after the start of the Great War there was a need to turn Britain's factories over to the production of military equipment and in 1916 the government took control of the AEC factory in Blackhorse Lane, Walthamstow.

An AEC 'B' Type Bus converted into a mobile pigeon loft.

AEC 'B' Type buses on the Western Front moving troops.

As the factory had been set up to handle mass production they were able to produce over nine hundred 'B'-type troop-carriers and around ten thousand three ton Y-type lorries by the time war had ended. At the beginning, due to the high demand for military transport, some 'B'-types found their way to the front in an unmodified state still in their London General Omnibus livery. Later deliveries to the front had their windows removed and boarded up and the overall colour was khaki.

Apart from moving troops, some 'B'-types were converted into pigeon lofts to house carrier pigeons that were vital for communication purposes, especially when enemy shells had cut through the Allied trench telephone lines. Others buses were turned into mobile anti-aircraft gun platforms and by the end of the war the 'B'-type ferried many grateful British Tommies home.

REFERENCES

Baldwin, Nick, AEC – The Early Years (*The Vintage Commercial Vehicle Magazine*, vol.3, no.9, July/August 1987)

Day, John R., *The Story of the London Bus* (L.T. Publications, 1973)

Dennis, John A., *AEC – 50 Years*, AEC Gazette, (November/December 1962)

Lewis, Jim, *London's Lea Valley, Britain's Best Kept Secret*, Phillimore & Company Limited, (Chichester 1999)

Thomson, L.A., *By Bus Coach and Tram in Walthamstow* (Walthamstow Antiquarian Society, 1971)

Townsin, Alan, The Way it was at AEC (*The Vintage Commercial Vehicle Magazine*, vol.4, no.18, January/February 1989)

Note

I should like to thank Lindsay Collier and members of the Pump House Museum, Walthamstow for providing various images to illustrate this chapter.

Alexandra Palace, Wood Green

Alexandra Palace began life in May 1873 as 'The People's Palace' and was purposely designed to be a great recreational facility for the general public. The inspiration for the building came after the Great Exhibition of 1851 when the temporary Crystal Palace was erected in London's Hyde Park.

Alexandra Palace having the iconic television mast erected c. 1935.

Sixteen days after 'The Peoples Palace' was built and thousands of visitors had streamed through its doors, tragedy struck when the building was consumed by fire. However, in May 1875 the new Palace rose Phoenix-like from the ashes and opened its doors once again to introduce a Victorian public to a world of art, fun and culture.

Today's Alexandra Palace, now a prominent London landmark on the Lea Valley's western slopes, is probably better known as the birthplace of television. In November 1936 the British Broadcasting Corporation (BBC) began transmitting the world's first public service broadcasts of high-definition television (405-line monochrome) on the all-electronic EMI Marconi system.

In my earlier books I have documented the role of Alexandra Palace during the Second World War when the television transmitter was modified and used to jam the navigation systems of German aircraft on their way to bomb targets in Britain. However, what is probably less well known is the role of the building during the Great War.

During the Great War the palace provided temporary accommodation for some 38,000 refugees. Between 1914 and March 1915 the palace was used as a transit camp for Belgian refugees who had fled their country to escape the clutches of the invading German Army. After the refugees had left, the palace and park became an internment camp.

After 1915, Alexandra Palace became a civilian internment camp. The picture shows beds and personal effects in the Great Hall.

It has been recorded by a local historian that in the year 1916 the camp held 'over 2,200 prisoners of war, including 1,600 German and some 700 Austrian soldiers'. However, later research has shown that the inmates were probably not military personnel. Dr Maggie Butt, who has recently written a book, *Ally Pally Prison Camp*, suggests that 'Alexandra Palace was a civilian internment camp throughout the First World War. Most of the prisoners had English wives and children and owned businesses in Britain – it was only their passports made them "enemy aliens"'. Among this group were artists, musicians and writers not to mention those who had fled Germany to escape conscription.

Cooking for the civilian internees at Alexandra Palace.

A Christmas card produced for internees at Alexandra Palace to send home to family and friends.

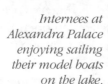

Internees at Alexandra Palace enjoying sailing their model boats on the lake.

A plaque on the building placed there in June 2000 by the Anglo-German History Society claims that 17,000 German and other civilian prisoners of war were interned at Alexandra between 1914 and 1919. As later research has suggested, the term 'prisoners of war' should not have been used on the plaque at Alexander Palace as it was not a 'prison camp'. Those who resided there should have been classified as 'internees' or in transit.

A plaque of remembrance placed on the wall at Alexandra Palace by the Anglo-German Family History Society.

REFERENCES

Butt, Maggie, *Ally Pally Prison Camp* (Oversteps Books, Kingsbridge, 2011)

Gay, Ken, *A Palace on the Hill, A History of Alexandra Palace and Park* (Hornsey Historical Society, 1994)

Harris, Janet, *Alexandra Palace: A Hidden History* (History Press, Stroud, 2005)

Personal conversation with the Curator of Bruce Castle Museum, December 2013

Note

There seems to be some confusion over the terms 'prison camp' and 'prisoner of war' and also association with military personnel when articles and books have been written about Alexandra Palace. It is probably fair to say that some of the civilian internees at Alexandra Palace saw themselves as prisoners of war and over the years the terminology has become a little muddied in its interpretation. To date, I have not come across any evidence that would suggest that military personnel were imprisoned at Alexandra Palace. Consulting the photograph records of the time show most internees smartly dressed in civilian clothes and not incarcerated behind barbed wire fencing. None of the internees are dressed in prisoner type uniforms or are seen with armed guards in close proximity.

It has also been noted that in a later edition of a popular local history book the author has removed the reference to 'soldiers' being imprisoned at Alexandra Palace!

Note 2

I should like to thank Deborah Hedgecock, the Curator of Bruce Castle Museum, Tottenham, for her valuable advice when writing this section of the book.

J A Prestwich (J.A.P), Tottenham

At the age of twenty, John Alfred Prestwich (1874–1952) first set up business in 1895 as the Prestwich Manufacturing Company, making electrical fittings and scientific instruments, in a greenhouse at his parents' home, Warmington House, High Road, Tottenham. Young John also seems to have inherited a love of things photographic from his father and this extra skill would appear timely. When the moving picture craze hit Britain in the late 19th century, Prestwich was able to combine his photographic knowledge with his engineering skills to produce a range of equipment for the burgeoning movie industry. For a young man he must have had considerable confidence in his abilities as he invented, designed and manufactured a range of movie cameras, printers and projectors and also machines for perforating, measuring and cutting film. His love of the subject was so deep that he also became expert at the art of making and showing films.

Prestwich married in 1898 and with his bride moved into their new home 3 Lansdowne Road, Tottenham. At about this time he also acquired the premises next door, number 1 Lansdowne Road, for his workshop. With the growing success of his business Prestwich was quickly running out

JAP workshop Lansdowne Rd c. 1895.

of space and when an adjacent disused chapel came onto the market he jumped at the opportunity and bought it. By 1903, with a workforce now totalling fifty, Prestwich turned to another of his earlier loves, that of designing and building engines.

One of his fist commercially successful J.A.P. 293cc engines was taken up by the Triumph Cycle Company of Birmingham and incorporated into one of their early motorcycles at a time when the embryonic motorcycle industry was going through an uncertain phase in the vehicle's popularity. It has been argued that it was due to the reliability of the J.A.P. engine, that had been manufactured to exacting standards of tolerance, that gave the buying public the confidence to invest in this new form of transport and 'kick-started' the Birmingham motorcycle industry into existence.

J A Prestwich & Company's early factory on the left and house to the right, Lansdowne Rd, Tottenham c. 1900.

As motorcycling grew in popularity demand for J.A.P. engines increased and this caused Prestwich to concentrate his engineering expertise on manufacturing engines for the burgeoning industry and not to compete against Triumph by producing his own branded machines. Production at Lansdowne Road soon outstripped the relatively limited workshop space and in January 1911 manufacturing was transferred to a new purpose-built factory in Northumberland Park, Tottenham which had been designed with future expansion in mind. The move was to prove extremely timely as during the lead-up to the Great War, the British Government began to increase the level of contracts placed with the company and when war was eventually declared the factory received further government orders for a range of munitions, aircraft parts and, not surprisingly, motorcycle engines.

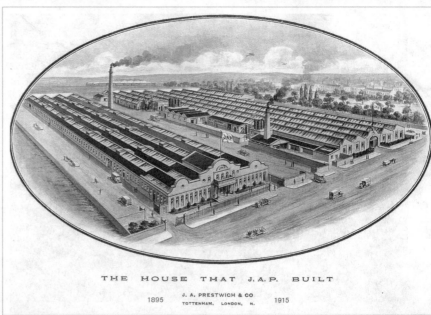

Top right: Women munitions workers at the J.A.P. factory, Northumberland Park, Tottenham c.1915.

Right: An artist's impression of the J.A.P factory complex, Northumberland Park, Tottenham c. 1915.

Like many other companies in Britain when war broke out, J.A.P. manufacturing suffered in two ways. First there was the loss of skilled workers as men were drafted into the armed forces and women had to be trained to take their place. And second, exports of equipment to countries who had sided with Germany against the Allies were banned. While this was the same for all British manufacturers the effects were probably more severely felt by J.A.P. as their engines, which had gained an international reputation, enjoyed a healthy export market. The extent of the downturn in overseas business can be judged by the fact that when hostilities ceased former German customers returned and placed annual orders for around 35,000 engines.

J.A.P. Factory Northumberland Park c. 1950.

REFERENCES

Buchanan, D.J., *The J.A.P. Story, 1895 – 1951*, J.A. Prestwich, Northumberland Park, (Tottenham, 1951)

Clew, Jeff, *J.A.P. – The Vintage Years,* (Haines Publishing Group, Yeovil, 1985)

Clew, Jeff, *J.A.P. – The End of an Era* (Haines Publishing Group, Yeovil, 1988)

Lewis, Jim, *London's Lea Valley, Britain's Best Kept Secret* (Phillimore & Company Limited, Chichester, 1999)

The British Oxygen Company (BOC), Edmonton

In 1902 a manufacturing company called Aerators Limited bought three acres of land on the south side of Water Lane, Edmonton (now Angel Road, the A406) to build a new factory. When established locally the company name

Early plan of the British Oxygen Company's works at Edmonton; the site on Angel Road covered almost 20 acres.

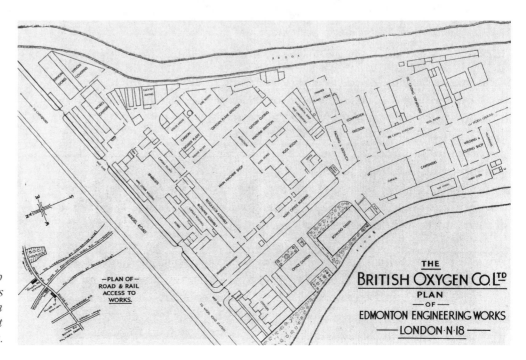

changed to Sparklets Limited after a popular brand of soda syphon they were manufacturing at the time. On completion of the new factory the owners named the building Prana after another of their soda syphon brands. At the time one of the main products manufactured at the factory was a bulb that dissolved carbon dioxide into the contents of the soda syphon, thereby producing sparkling soda water or aerated water as the Victorians had called it.

The invention of the soda syphon bulb was heavily advertised as a simple and cheap way of producing soda water that anyone could make. Prior to the bulb system becoming available soda water was sold by the bottle and was considered an expensive luxury. The soda syphon became a popular way of enhancing alcoholic beverages in many countries around the world particularly in those far-away exotic destinations that enjoyed the heat of the midday sun.

Sparklets soda syphon covering shop, BOC, Edmonton c. 1930

An advertisement for the Sparklets soda syphon, placed in a New Zealand periodical.

An early Sparklets soda syphon.

At the time of the Great War many factories came under government control and were required to manufacture many different products including ammunition. Sparklets Limited was given contracts to produce the 'Pomeroy' 0.303 small arms round for the Royal Flying Corps (RFC) that was usually mixed with the standard round in the aircraft's machine guns. This ammunition was incendiary and specifically designed to ignite the hydrogen carried by Zeppelins that were attacking targets on the Home and other Fronts. Interestingly the cartridges became known as Sparklets, probably because a successful 'kill' would light up the sky!

After the war the British Oxygen Company took over Sparklets Limited and later became BOC Process Plants which specialised in the manufacture of a range of Vacuum Insulated Tanks (VITs) and other associated equipment for the liquid gas industry. The site finally closed in the late 1980s and has been replaced by a retail park.

Operator standing beside large boring mill in the BOC machine shop c. 1930

View of the British Oxygen Company's Edmonton works from the air c. 1930.
Note the lack of traffic on Angel Road in the foreground.

REFERENCES

Author Unknown, Around the Group in 100 Years (BOC Process Plants, 1986)

Author Unknown, A History of BOC Process Plants Edmonton (BOC Process Plants, c.1995)

Lewis, Jim, *London's Lea Valley, More Secrets Revealed* (Phillimore & Company Limited, Chichester, 2001)

The London Small Arms Company Limited, Bow

Originally founded in 1856 as The London Armoury Company Limited by a group of London gunsmiths, the company went out of business as a result of losses sustained after the American Civil War of 1861. The company was dissolved in 1866 and was reconstituted as The London Small Arms Company Limited (LSA Co.). In making this change the new company hoped that, along with other groupings of private gun contractors like the Birmingham Small Arms Company (BSA), it would be in a stronger position to compete for government contracts and also to challenge the dominance of the government-controlled Royal Small Arms Factory at Enfield Lock.

An early engraving of the London Small Arms Company, Bow.

While it would not be allowed in Britain today under competition law, from 1867 onwards the Birmingham and London companies agreed to fix wage rates and product prices. Also they agreed to share contracts for rifle production. However, unlike its Birmingham counterpart, the LSA Company did not seek to diversify its production and throughout its lifetime it remained a relatively small enterprise. As an example of its manufacturing output: immediately prior to the Great War the Royal Small Arms Factory was manufacturing one thousand rifles per week and repairing a similar amount, the Birmingham Small Arms Company were producing seven hundred and fifty rifles per week and the LSA Company were only managing two hundred and fifty.

A Lee Enfield Mk III, manufactured by the London Small Arms Company.

A London Small Arms Company advertisement for sporting rifles; note the lower Lee Enfield image (chambered to take 0.22 ammunition).

At the outbreak of the Great War the government asked both the Birmingham and London companies to dramatically increase their rifle output but unfortunately the LSA Company had built on all available land and could not create further manufacturing space.

A Bow heritage trail plaque that commemorates the site of the Gunmakers Arms and its later history.

REFERENCES

Author unknown, *The London Small Arms Company Limited* (Drew & Hopwood, Birmingham, July 1906)

Author unknown, *The London Small Arms Company Limited,* (The Archive Guide, The Royal Bank of Scotland Group)

Remington Cartridge box.

Remington catalogue 1920.

Remington Arms-Union Metallic Cartridge Company, Brimsdown

The brief story that I am about to relate can be classed as something of a mystery. When researching the material for this book I was passed an article that appeared in the *International Ammunition Association Journal* of July – August 1994 which was entitled 'Brimsdown, Remington's English Loading Factory'. The publication appears to be aimed at enthusiasts and collectors of weapons and gun cartridges. As someone who has been involved with writing and lecturing about the industries of the Lea Valley for more years than I can remember, the Brimsdown Remington Company was a firm that I had no knowledge of operating in the region.

According to the article Remington's English Loading Factory, which seems to be the name preferred by the American parent company, was responsible for loading empty paper cartridge cases imported from the USA with powder and shot manufactured in Britain. The company was also responsible for 'importations of rim fire and centre fire ammunition and sporting firearms from our United States plants'. From what I have been able to piece together it would seem that the factory, or the Brimsdown site, was in the hands of the Remington Company approximately between 1912 and the 1940s.

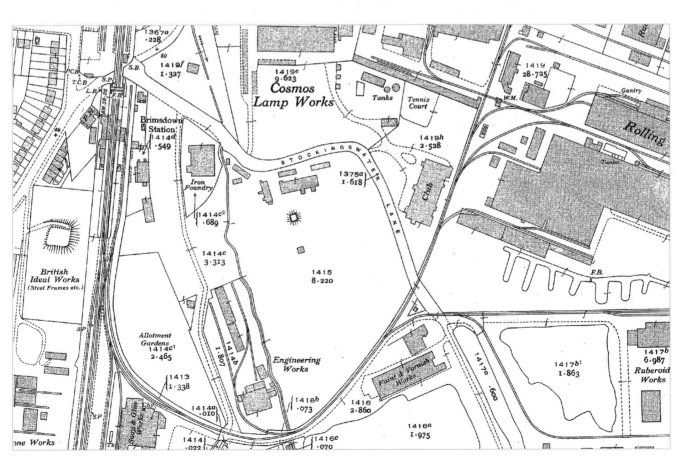

Map showing Remington Brimsdown site, south of Cosmos lamp works, 1939.

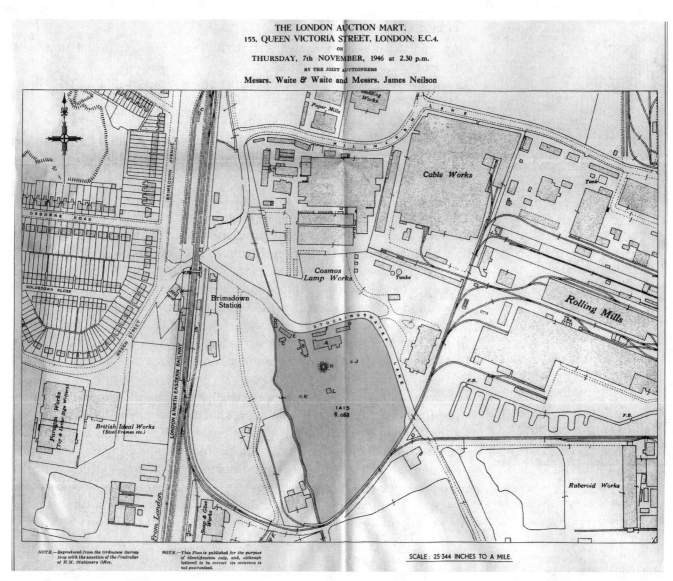

THE LONDON AUCTION MART,
155, QUEEN VICTORIA STREET, LONDON, E.C.4.
ON
THURSDAY, 7th NOVEMBER, 1946 at 2.30 p.m.
BY THE JOINT AUCTIONEERS
Messrs. Waite & Waite and Messrs. James Neilson

SCALE: 25·344 INCHES TO A MILE.

Map from the auctioneers catalogue, showing Remington, Brimsdown site prior to sale in 1946.

Interestingly the author of the article has included a map of the Brimsdown site which shows the Remington factory on the south side of Stockingswater Lane where the positions of a number of buildings are also given. One of these buildings is described as the 'Nissen' Store Hut, 60ft x 16ft having a concrete floor'. By sheer coincidence, when I worked in Enfield for the radio and television manufacturer Thorn EMI Ferguson, I used to occasionally visit our Mazda cathode ray tube factory that was located approximately on the same site as the former Remington factory. Therefore, the story of the early Nissen hut which had been used by engineers as an Applications Laboratory when Mazda moved onto the site in the early 1930s, was familiar to me.

Recalling this long-held memory got me wondering. Could this Nissan hut be the same one that had been used by Remington? After all, it would seem unlikely that an electronics manufacturer coming to the Brimsdown site in the 1930s would deliberately choose to build such a hut for a laboratory. It would seem more likely that the new resident would have taken over an existing building, like the hut, and adapted it for laboratory use.

To confirm my supposition I telephoned one of my former Thorn EMI colleagues, Dennis Harvey, who was able to confirm that he had worked in the Mazda Nissen hut laboratory as an apprentice in the mid 1940s. Dennis also confirmed that although the hut had been lined and modified internally the exterior of the building was rather shabby denoting that it was not

The Hut, Mazda applications laboratory, Brimsdown, 1932.

particularly new. However, Dennis had no knowledge of the hut's association with Remington; in fact he was unaware that the American company had previously occupied the site. Another Thorn colleague, Bob Burrows, who had also worked with Dennis in the 'hut' had no knowledge of the former Remington connections either.

Fortunately Dennis was able to find an early photograph of the 'hut' which triggered a vision in his memory. On viewing the photograph he remarked 'for me, it is remarkable to see the hut standing in the middle of an otherwise empty field because it was later surrounded by all the industrial buildings comprising the Mazda valve plant'. Therefore, it would seem reasonable to assume that Mazda inherited the hut when they took over the site.

As the Remington story is virtually hitherto unknown, I should like to take this opportunity to call upon the inquisitive reader to take up the research challenge and fill in the missing gaps in our Lea Valley history. One important question that should be addressed is: did the British government during the period of the Great War take over this American manufacturer and commit them to war work?

REFERENCES

Author unknown, Enfield's Industries, (*Enfield Gazette*, 24 September 1926)

Hedlund. Dale, J., Brimsdown, Remington's English Loading Factory (*International Ammunition Association Journal*, July–August, 1994)

Harvey, Dennis, *Private conversation and correspondence* (8th January, 2014)

Note

The Nissen hut was designed by Major Peter Norman Nissen of the Royal Engineers. After the prototype was approved by the military the hut went into production in 1916. During the final period of the Great War some 100,000 huts were produced.

Note 2

I should like to take this opportunity to thank Kate Godfrey of the Enfield Local History Unit for her considerable patience and help during the writing of this section. Also I should like to thank Jackie Butcher and Patricia Graham for collating information from the Enfield archive that has helped the writing of this section enormously.

Lebus Furniture, Tottenham Hale

When Louis Lebus died in 1879 the business, then in London's east end, was inherited by his twenty-seven-year-old son Harris. After a number of moves to larger premises to keep up with expanding business the decision was

The Lebus factory site on the south side of Ferry Lane before the drying sheds and the north factory were built.

taken, in 1900, to build a new factory on a thirteen-and-a-half-acre green-field site adjacent to the River Lea and away from the congested east end. The site chosen for the new furniture factory was the then relatively peaceful Tottenham Hale. Subsequently extra land was purchased and the site almost trebled to around forty acres. To maintain a London presence a former Lebus factory building in Tabernacle Street was converted to showrooms to display the widening range of furniture.

At the outbreak of the Great War, like many other manufacturing industries, Lebus found itself engaged in government contracts to produce essential products for the Allied Forces. Contracts for ammunition boxes, military tents and sections of aircraft were received. However, the military call to arms saw skilled men volunteering for the armed services and this in turn caused serious labour shortages on the shop floor. The answer was to recruit women and after a period of training it was found that the new recruits were capable of carrying out skilled work on a par with their male counterparts. This was how most firms coped with labour shortages during the Great War and, for that matter, the war that followed in 1939.

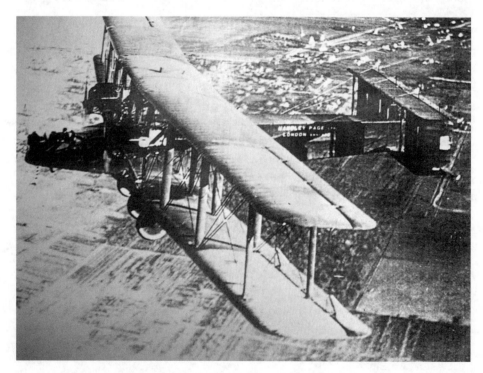

A WW1 Handley Page bomber, large sections of these aircraft were manufactured at Lebus.

Handley Page fuselage assembly shop.

Ammunition box construction at Lebus during WW1.

Doping wing of model 0400 Handley Page bomber at Lebus during WW 1.

Lebus tent bottom makers during WW1.

Women were employed in the manufacture of tents for the troops, ammunition boxes and other wartime essentials. They were also involved in the covering and doping (a process of applying a varnish-like substance to a covering fabric) of aircraft. This process made the aircraft's covering taut which enhanced the integrity of the airframe; it also made the fabric waterproof. The application of dope was not a particularly pleasant or healthy job for the women operatives but it was an essential part of early aircraft construction. Dope was applied to the wings and bodies of heavy bombers like the Handley Page 0/100 and the V/1500 bi-plane that were manufactured at the Lebus factory. Women at Lebus also covered and doped the Vickers Vimy, another twin-engine heavy bomber.

The contribution made by women workers on the Home Front should never be underestimated. It has often been said that battles at the Front are won on the shop floor. In other words, without the manufacture of arms and equipment the battle would be lost or could never have begun, nor could a country be defended.

Vickers Vimy wings being covered with fabric during WW1

A roof top view of the Lebus factory c. 1950s.

REFERENCES

Lewis, Jim, *Regeneration and Innovation, Invention and Reinvention in the Lea Valley* (Libri Publishing Limited, Oxford, 2011)

Massil, William, *Immigrant Furniture Workers in London, 1881 – 1939* (The Jewish Museum in association with the Geffrye Museum, London, 1997)

CONCLUSION

In this book we have looked at a representative number of Lea Valley industries and other regional events that have influenced the outcome of the Great War. Perhaps the most significant of these was the invention of the diode valve by Professor Ambrose Fleming which, unbeknown to him at the time, would cause a revolution in the communications technology that followed. Ironically, the consequences of helping us improve the way we communicate over long distances has allowed countries around the world to engage in wars that have become increasingly savage and bitter. Sadly this has led to the current worldwide refugee crisis that has reached unprecedented proportions.

On a less sombre note, given more time, it should be possible to uncover additional Lea Valley stories that have been lost. I would therefore like to take this opportunity to encourage students of history and those budding Sherlock Homes to take up the detective work before our heritage becomes lost forever in the mists of time.